SOVIET SPACE
TECHNOLOGY

SOVIET
SPACE
TECHNOLOGY

BY ALFRED J. ZAEHRINGER

HARPER & BROTHERS, PUBLISHERS, NEW YORK

CONTENTS

LIST OF
ILLUSTRATIONS

FOREWORD

It is always interesting to see a factual assessment made of the achievements of other societies in a scientific field. In these days, it is particularly stimulating to see such a study made about rocket and space efforts.

This book by Alfred J. Zaehringer about Soviet space and rocket hardware intended for engineers, scientists, and knowledgeable laymen, covers a rather extended period of time.

The Soviets, as well as the Western world, have made substantial —even sensational—advances in rocket and space hardware. Without question, even greater accomplishments in the hardware department will be forthcoming for a long time. Eventually, however, these improvements will be in the form of refinements to the then existing spacecraft, rather than increases in size of thrust and payload. These refinements will include nuclear and ion engines, as well as greater reliability over all.

This book provides a generous source of information that should be of interest to rocket and space men everywhere.

Wernher von Braun
Director
George C. Marshall Space Flight Center (NASA)
Huntsville, Alabama

AUTHOR'S PREFACE

This book was written to provide a single source of information concerning Soviet rocket and space technology. In 1952 the author heard a talk given by George Sutton on rockets behind the Iron Curtain. The large efforts then shaping up were evident. However, there seemed to be little of a centralized nature. Everything available on Soviet rockets seemed to be scattered. Concluding that a centralized effort was really under way, the author worked out a possible family of missiles, based on existing technology and military needs. This allowed a classification system, or a label, for an indefinite, nebulous product that might never be seen by Western eyes but whose growing influence must surely be evidenced in a short time. This classification system has proved to be relatively accurate and finally has fallen into place as a result of the Sputnik and Lunik launchings and some of the missiles actually displayed during the famous November 1957 parade in Moscow's Red Square.

Up to now there has been no one place to turn to for a complete picture of Soviet rocket and space technology. The author had to collect the bits and pieces—to go through literally thousands of pages of scientific (and nonscientific) literature, listen to oral reports in person and over radio and TV, look at pictures, find any material he could lay his hands on. It is doubtful if we will ever get a complete picture from the Soviets themselves. For one thing, most developments fall into military areas and these are traditionally kept secret. The research areas are so general as to offer few direct clues, although indirect information can be gleaned. Probably the Soviets themselves could not assemble a complete picture because of the vastness of the programs. In many cases, the author has had to work backward—that is, by taking a given performance feat and a given technology, design a possible rocket. Sometimes you are way off and other times you can be very close. That is the way the ball orbits in this game! It should be remembered that the Soviets have shown us very little; the rest is shrouded in the area of hypothesized conjecture.

The author wishes to thank Dr. Donald J. Ritchie of the Research Laboratories, Bendix Corporation, for his valuable suggestions and comments, and also Mr. F. J. Krieger of the Rand Corporation for background material. The work of my secretary, Rita Gazdag, for the grueling first draft typing and research on the Soviet educational system is deeply appreciated. Mr. James Wells, of my aero group, has given many practical engineering comments. Also to be acknowledged is the work of Jane High for grammatical and general comments. Many industrial and publications groups also furnished information. In particular, publications of the American Chemical Society, the American Rocket Society, and the American Ordnance Association have been useful in their analyses of Soviet space and technological developments. Other material has come from the United States Air Force, the United States Army, and the United States Navy, plus the public service groups, the United States Congress, the Department of Commerce, the Central Intelligence Agency, and the National Science Foundation. The conclusions and opinions developed here are those of the author.

Alfred J. Zaehringer
Wyandotte, Michigan
December, 1960

CHAPTER 1

FOUNDATION

THE FOUNDATION for present-day Soviet space technology actually is to be found back in the czarist days. The early freedom accorded the scientists in the times of the czars was simply carried over into the Soviet system. It is this salient fact that is responsible for the present high level of Soviet space efforts. The procedure was to give the scientists freedom and security and then let them present their ideas to engineers; then back these engineers with tools, materials, and direct government confidence. According to the Soviets it is in this manner that science and technology will forge a new world influence—an invulnerable Soviet technical domination. Thus, the Soviets have not needed to mask any inferiorities in astronautics. Although they did not invent rockets, the early Soviet recognition of their importance certainly played a major role in creating today's world of the Space Age!

Pre-Revolution

At the close of the seventeenth century, a factory was opened in Russia for manufacturing gunpowder rockets; these solid rockets were used as skyrockets for holiday and celebrational pyrotechnic displays. This was the basis for future development of rockets in Russia. Signal rockets produced at this factory were used by Russian troops from 1717 to 1867 with almost no changes. Two of the developers of Russian gunpowder rockets as weapons were the military engineers Alexander Zasyadko (1779-1837) and Konstantin Konstantinov (1818-1871). A war rocket was designed and tested by Zasyadko in St. Petersburg in 1817; this engineer was later promoted to the rank of major general. The first rocket company in Russia was founded at St. Petersburg in 1826. Thousands of Zasyadko's rockets were used in military campaigns in the Russo-Turkish War of 1828-1829 and in the war of the Caucasus. However, quantities of Congreve rockets (designed by the British Sir William Congreve) had already been used in the War of 1812. It is interesting to note that the American, William Hale, improved the Congreve rocket and it was these rockets that were referred to in the "Star Spangled Banner's" the "rocket's red glare" in the bombardment of Fort McHenry in 1812.

Konstantin Konstantinov is said to be the founder of experimental rocketry. He advocated rocket standardization and applied scientific principles in testing rockets. It was he who devised a ballistic pendulum for static testing of a rocket. Later, the American pioneer, Dr. Robert H. Goddard, began his rocket work by using a ballistic pendulum and showed that a rocket could and did work better in a vacuum.

There are scattered references to rockets in the Russian literature of pre-revolutionary days. At the end of the nineteenth century, I. V. Meshchersky worked on the dynamics of variable masses. These dynamics are directly applicable to the rocket which trades mass for increased velocity. However, it remained for Konstantin Eduardovich Ziolkovsky to propose the scientific foundations of rocketry and space flight.

Born September 5, 1858 at Ljewsk, Ziolkovsky grew up in Rjasan, one of the smallest provinces of European Russia. Because of deafness Konstantin had difficulty in his schoolwork at Rjasan and was tutored by his mother in mathematics and physics. Early in his childhood a friend brought him a balloon.

This was his first experience with a flight vehicle, and the boy became so interested in the physics of flight that he worked out the mathematical principle of ballooning. Later he improvised a hydrogen-filled airship; and at the age of sixteen he began to experiment with metal balloons.

In the winter of 1874, when he was seventeen, Konstantin went to Moscow to study. As he gazed at the eighty-meter high clock tower at the gates of Kremlin Palace, his thoughts turned to space flight.

During his school days Ziolkovsky used to talk with his friends about the possibilities of space flight, but times were hard. His allowance was only ten rubles a month and he had to spend ninety kopeks of this for bread just to keep alive. That was all he would allow himself for food. Many times he went cold and hungry to buy the necessary chemicals and apparatus to continue his experiments. "My stomach was filled with black bread," he said, "but my head was filled with great dreams and plans."

For three years he studied physics, astronomy, mechanics, and geometry. All during these years he sought a propulsion method which would enable vehicles to carry man to the planets. Since air was not available in space, a new mechanism must be found. Finally, one day he thought of harnessing the action and reaction principle. The rocket was the way to space! He reached this conclusion in the year 1876. It was also in 1876 that A. Hall discovered the moons of Mars and Schiaparelli, told of seeing canals on Mars. This was thirty years before the Wright Brothers made their first airplane flight.

There were three more years of study for Ziolkovsky at Moscow. In 1882 he returned to the Kaluga district as a professor of mathematics and physics. At last he was able to pursue his ideas. Through the renowned chemist Dimitri Mendeleev (who worked out the periodic system of elements) Ziolkovsky's works were presented to the three hundred year old Society for

Physics and Chemistry at St. Petersburg (now Leningrad). Eventually he was invited to become a member of this distinguished group.

It is said that Ziolkovsky also conducted experiments on electrical discharge systems but was forced to discontinue them because they made his hair stand on end and caused sparks to fly from his fingers.

He was concerned with actual flying models but lacked testing facilities. He then began to work on the balloon as a transportation vehicle. His proposals in this field are now in the Polytechnic Museum in Moscow and deal with balloons and steerable airships.

Mendeleev suggested that Ziolkovsky come to Moscow to pursue his experiments further, but he chose to remain at Kaluga, 160 kilometers to the southeast, where he could continue with his work at his own pace.

The German, Lilienthal, also was convinced that man could fly, but his first airplane was made of wood and other frangible materials. Ziolkovsky was the first to conceive of the all-metal aircraft and to propose methods for its construction. He also envisioned the completely closed cabin and the possibilities of a light, strong gasoline engine for safer aircraft flight.

Even though Ziolkovsky's ideas seemed workable in theory they were not considered practical and at first he could gain little support. It was not until he received a subsidy of 470 rubles from the Academy of Sciences that his financial problems were solved.

In his room at Kaluga he constructed the first wind tunnel in Russia. With these primitive facilities, he began the measurement of air resistance and developed mathematical relations in these experiments.

During this time he wrote a fantasy called "To the Moon, a Fantastic Trip" which appeared in a magazine *Round the World*. In 1893 it was published separately in Moscow as a booklet. Two years later his *Dreams of Earth and Heaven* appeared; in 1896 his small work *Can World Beings Exist on Other Planets?* At this time, Ziolkovsky first began his experiments on rockets. However, much of his work remained unknown outside of Russia.

A breakthrough came when Ziolkovsky received a brochure from an obscure inventor, Alexander Petrovitch Fiodorov, which was called, "A New Flight Method, the Rocket Principle for Interplanetary Flights." Ziolkovsky, who had thought of this years ago, set about correcting its many mistakes. He asked himself: "What is space?" The rocket in cosmic space must have air in a cabin for its passengers and the air in this cabin must be replenished with fresh oxygen. However, the chief problem was propulsion. In empty space the reaction principle seemed workable. The rocket must be greater and more powerful than the existing small solid propellant rockets. Greater performance on the part of the rocket, however, could be obtained through higher exhaust velocities of the burning gasses. In order to obtain these high velocities, solids must be replaced by liquid propellants.

A successor and former pupil of Ziolkovsky, Yu. V. Kondratyuk, later wrote that a composite interplanetary ship should be comprised of several stages

of gradually decreasing size; mainly aluminum, silicon, and magnesium serve as construction materials; as far as possible, parts requiring special heat resistance are made of suitable kinds of graphite or carborundum; stages becoming unnecessary because of their size, because of the reduced mass of the rocket, are not discarded but are dismantled and go . . . to be reduced and melted in order to be used later as the chemical components of fuel.

It is interesting to note that about 80 per cent of present United States missiles use aluminum as a construction material; in the United States Redstone and Jupiter long-range rocket missiles, 90 per cent of the total airframe weight is aluminum. Even more striking is the fact that both graphite and ceramics such as carborundum are now used for high temperature rocket engine components (many solid rockets use graphite nozzles, while the Nike, for example, used a ceramic combustion chamber). And the use of powdered aluminum as a fuel in the new high-performance solid propellants is an accomplished fact.

Therefore, the proposed problem for flight into cosmic space envolved into the necessity for a liquid propellant rocket. Ziolkovsky was the first person in the world to mention such a rocket. However, a mere scaling up of the rocket was not sufficient. The propellant weight of the empty rocket had to be reduced as much as possible. Herein entered the mass ratio problem. Ziolkovsky calculated the exhaust velocities and mass ratio for liquid rockets traveling into cosmic space.

About this time Ziolkovsky wrote a paper, "Investigations of World Spaces with Reaction Devices." He sent it to the *Scientific Review* of which two of his friends, W. J. Assonov and Professor M. M. Philippov, were editors. The *Scientific Review* had already published not only articles by Mendeleev but by Marx, Engels, and Lenin as well, but Ziolkovsky's article did not appear until five years later—in 1903. In 1911 he published another work on the reaction apparatus; and in 1914 the results of his experiments in this field appeared as a news item in the *Moscow Journal* under the heading, "Contributions to Air Travel."

Post-Revolution

The October revolution of 1917 did little to diminish the efforts of the then sixty-year-old Ziolkovsky. Indeed, his contributions in the field rapidly increased. Three of his works were *Without Gravity, The Other Side of the World,* and *Wealth of the World.* The state press of Kaluga published his long contributions to scientific reviews in 1924 under the new title *The Rocket into Cosmic Space.* A year later the work of the German rocket pioneer, Hermann Oberth, was published in Munich under the title of *The Rocket into Planetary Space.*

Ziolkovsky continued to pour out works on rocket and space travel. Some of the titles are: *A Space Rocket and Its Experimental Preparation, The Trip into Space, Lines of Space Travel, The Reactionsmotor, Star Travels, The Vehicle for Star Travels.* It is strange, but this man Ziolkovsky never even saw a rocket in a test stand! However, his theoretical discussions of a liquid-cooled, bi-propellant rocket combustion chamber are very similar to the actual engines in use today.

In 1929 Ziolkovsky disciples founded a scientific organization for the systematic investigation of new rocket devices. It was called GIRD (initials of the Russian Words for "Group for the Study of Reactive Motion"). The Moscow branch was founded by Engineer I. P. Fortikov and was known as "Mosgird"; Professor N. A. Rynin and Dr. Ya. I. Perel'man formed the Leningrad branch, "Lengird."

A contemporary of Ziolkovsky, F. A. Tsander, conceived the idea of burning the no longer used metal hulls of space ships as fuels to further increase performance. Tsander built and fired a liquid oxygen-kerosene rocket engine in 1932. This same combination, incidentally, is believed to power most of the present-day large Soviet liquid missiles and space vehicles. In 1934 *Pravda* wrote of Tsander:

This man spent his life wonderfully! While still a boy, he reads with interest books and stories on astronomy. With his first-earned money he buys an astronomical telescope and often observes the planets and stars for several hours on end. While a university student in 1908, he makes calculations on the reactive engine. Marriage: children are born: the name of his daughter is Astra, the name of his son, Mercury. Every thought, every step manifests his aspiration for interplanetary flight!

At the end of 1920, at the Moscow Province Conference of Inventors, Tsander read a paper. V. I. Lenin, who was present at the Conference, became interested in the paper and rendered Tsander his support.

Here we see the very seeds of space flight becoming firmly implanted in the minds of influential Soviets: Tsander and Lenin, and then Ziolkovsky and Stalin. Early support for the rising Red Star—a future Red Star in space!

At the May Day demonstration of May 1, 1933, Ziolkovsky spoke on Radio Kaluga. At this time he was seventy-five years old and he said:

For forty years I have worked on the rocket principle and have established that flight to the planet Mars will be possible in the foreseeable future. Though the time scale is unknown, the idea will remain. Today I am sure vehicles will make interplanetary voyages.

On September 13, 1935, desperately ill and feeling that death was near, Ziolkovsky wrote:

I give all my works in the areas of rocket flight and interplanetary trips to the Bolshevik Party and to the Russian government the leading research of man's culture. I am certain that these works shall be successfully carried through.

This letter was read with great interest by Stalin himself, who promptly cabled back:

The Learned Scholar
Comrade Konstantin Eduardovich Ziolkovsky
Kaluga

My thanks for your letter and for your contributions to the Bolshevik Party and the Soviet Government. I wish you health and further successful work in your field. I shake your hand.

J. Stalin

Ziolkovsky dictated an answer:

Comrade Joseph Stalin
Moscow

I am touched by your cordial greeting. I feel that on such a day I will not have died.

Ziolkovsky

In his own trembling hand he added, "I thank Comrade Stalin for all the masses; above all, the masses thank."

At 10:30 P.M. on September 19, 1935, Ziolkovsky's life came to an end. At Oka (in the Tula region) there stands the simple obelisk tombstone of Ziolkovsky carved with the inscription: *Mankind shall not remain on earth forever.*

In summing up, the contributions of Konstantin Eduardovich Ziolkovsky are as follows:

In 1903 he proposed the first liquid propellant rocket engine.

He first worked out a mathematical theory for rocket flight.

He recognized that the oxygen-hydrogen propellant combination would be the most powerful performer.

He advanced the concept of the multi-staged rocket or as he called it a "rocket train." "I mean a combination of several similar reactive devices . . . only a part of this train travels into celestial space; the remaining portions, not having sufficient velocity, return to the earth."

Today, some fifty-seven years later, the United States is to use the same combination on its first huge booster combination, the Saturn. Upper stages will use oxygen-hydrogen.

Just prior to World War II Ziolkovsky's theoretical works were implemented into experimental areas by the Soviet government in a suburb of Moscow. During World War II when the Germans approached Moscow, this laboratory was transferred to the Sverdlovsk region. German intelligence reports of this laboratory indicate that the Soviets left only buildings and offered no evidence of projects or actual hardware.

After Ziolkovsky's death, writings on rockets and space flight were evident even under the oppressive shadow of Josef Stalin. M. K. Tikhonravov and Ari A. Shternfeld (a recent winner of the International Prize for the Promotion of Astronautics) were prominent writers. Recently such writers as K. A. Gil'zin, B. V. Lyapunov, and Yu. S. Khlevtsevich have written in the area of rockets and space flight.

In the thirties the visions of Ziolkovsky were further implemented by co-workers. For example, Tsander constructed two rocket motors of 11 to 110 pounds of thrust; in 1924 Tsander had proposed a metal space vehicle. In the period of 1931-1936 the Soviet designer Glushko designed and built rocket engines of 300 to 600 pounds of thrust. Another Russian rocket pioneer, N. A. Rynin, compiled his astronautical encyclopedia in the Soviet Union during the period 1928-1932.

Also in the thirties, several groups conducted test stand firings of liquid propellant rocket engines. The Glushko engines operated, for example, on kerosene and nitric acid. Other static test works which formed the basis for large postwar liquid rocket engines used liquid oxygen with such typical fuels as gasoline, kerosene, benzene, and toluene. It is believed that in 1934 the Soviet government officially began sponsoring rocket research on a centralized basis. In 1932 the German government centralized its rocket research program under the directorship of the then Colonel Walter R. Dornberger and his young assistant, Wernher von Braun. It was not until 1939 (but did not get into high gear until 1942) that rocket research was undertaken by the government of the United States (this was the famous GALCIT Project initiated at the California Institute of Technology under the leadership of Theodore von Karman and General H. H. Arnold).

A meteorological rocket attained an altitude of 6 miles in 1935 and by 1940 the Soviets had an engine developing 330 pounds of thrust; this engine powered an all-metal rocket airplane. Thus did the dreams of Ziolkovsky finally come true!

However, there were some development projects on long-range lines; Glushko's engine was mated with the Winged Rocket 212 during 1937-1939. This winged rocket very much resembled the larger German V-1: both were launched from an inclined launching track with the aid of a small solid propellant rocket booster.

Thus, prior to World War II, the Soviet's work in rocketry

had produced small liquid rocket engines of under 1,000 pounds of thrust and solid propellant rocket work was almost non-existent. This was almost exactly the status of United States rocket work! By World War II, the Germans, on the other hand, were well along the road in the development of the long-range V-2 bombardment ballistic rocket. Then, when the Germans attacked Poland and the Russians concluded a pact with the Nazis, it looked as though the mechanistic German military sciences would be coupled with the efforts of the massive Red Bear. Less than a year later, Germany was at war with the USSR. German efforts were intensified especially with regard to long-range rockets. On the other hand, the work of the United States and the USSR ran almost parallel—both concentrated on producing millions of short-range artillery rockets.

World War II

The deep penetration of mobile German forces into the USSR necessitated development of large numbers of antitank and general artillery rockets. For this reason, not much came of early Soviet liquid engine work (Table 1). However, largely through the establishment of early rocket facilities and through the use of standard ballistic technology coupled with the availability of gun propellants which could be used for artillery purposes, the Soviets did succeed in turning out a wide variety of functional rocket weapons. Even today, only meager information is available on Soviet World War II rockets. Apparently little technical information was shared between the United States and the USSR even though the powers were allies. Evidently these Soviet weapons (Table 2) were an all-Soviet product. However, there is good reason to believe that the Soviets were quick to adapt the German rocket weapons that they captured and felt they could use. A standard rocket propellant at this time was known simply as "Russian Cordite." It had a composition of 56.5 per cent nitrocellulose (the nitrogen content of this nitrocellulose was 12.2 per cent), 28 per cent nitroglycerin, 11 per cent dinitrotoluene, and 4.5 per cent centralite. This formula was not too much different from that which was used by both the British and Americans. A typical American propellant of the time (JP "Ballistite") was quite similar in make-up and had the following composition: 52.2 per cent nitrocellulose (of 13.25 per cent nitrogen) 43.0 per cent nitroglycerin, 0.6 per cent diethyl phthalate, 1.25 per cent ethyl centralite, and 0.1 per cent nigrosine dye. Thus, United States and USSR propellant compositions were close by experimental coincidence and similar technology.

TABLE 1   EARLY SOVIET ROCKET ENGINES

Engine	Date	Designer	Thrust (lb)	Notes
OR-1	1930-1931	Tsander	11	
OR-2	1932	Tsander	110	
ORM-1	1931	Glushko		
ORM-5	1932	Glushko		
ORM-12	1932	Glushko		
ORM-50	1933	Glushko		
ORM-52	1933	Glushko	662	
ORM-65	1936	Glushko	342-386	Nitric acid/kerosene, used on Winged Rocket 212.
ZhRD			2640	Nitric acid/aniline, used as a rocket-assisted takeoff (RATO) unit.
Walter			440-3300	80 per cent hydrogen peroxide/hydrazine, used for auxiliary propulsion and RATO on aircraft. Soviet version of German engine.
RD-1	1943	Dushkin	651	
RD-1X3	1946	Lavochkin		
RD-3		Dushkin	1980	

TABLE 2   SOVIET WORLD WAR II ROCKETS

Name	Data
GVAI	An antiaircraft rocket. Unguided, projector-launched. Used a double-base solid propellant.
Katysusha	A surface-to-surface barrage (artillery) rocket. Had a diameter of 13 cm., weighed 42.2 kg. and carried a 21.8 lb. high-explosive warhead. Double-base solid propellant grain weighed 7.08 kg. and pushed this rocket to a speed of 305 meters per second (over 1,000 feet per second).
RS-82	This solid rocket was propelled by a grain of 1.01 kg. of double-base solid propellant. It had a diameter of 82 mm. and a total weight of 6.85 kg. It reached a velocity of 250 m/sec. and was widely used for surface-to-surface and antiaircraft barrage purposes. It was also adapted for aircraft use for air-to-surface strafing and for antitank operations.
RS-132	This solid rocket was similar to the RS-82 but it was much heavier (it weighed 23.1 kg.) and had a larger diameter (132 mm.). Propelled by 3.75 kg. of double-base propellant, it was used for many purposes.
RS-132A	A redesigned RS-132, this solid rocket had the same diameter but had a weight of 42 kg. and used 7.06 kg. of double-base propellant.
25KgAT	An aircraft-launched antitank rocket with a 55 lb. high-explosive warhead.
ATS	Developed around 1943, this was a small aircraft rocket (3.2 inch caliber) similar to the present US "Mighty Mouse" rocket. Using 2.2 lbs. of double-base propellant, the rocket had a length of 1.95 ft. and weighed 13.4 lbs. (its payload was 0.84 lbs. of high explosive). Maximum velocity of this rocket was 1,150 feet per second.

CHAPTER 2

CORNERSTONES

VARIOUS TYPES of cements were used to bind together a scattering of heterogeneous material to form the cornerstone of Soviet space technology. Two distinct types of mortars were the American and the German influence. These were added to the Russian influences outlined in Chapter 1. For these reasons, Soviet space technology is, by its very nature, a composite and complex structure.

German Influence

In Germany prior to World War II there were scattered rocket researchers. Much of the work was carried out by hobbyists who were rocket enthusiasts, and some were supported by German industry. Not long thereafter, the German Rocket Society consolidated many of these scattered programs. However, during the thirties, the lack of money did not allow elaborate work such as would be needed to develop powerful rockets more fully.

Wernher von Braun was a founding member of the rocket field at Berlin. This was a small rocket experimental station sponsored and financed by the German Rocket Society. At this time von Braun was attending school, but he also managed to assist Professor Oberth in carrying out experiments at Berlin-

Plötzensee aimed at the further development of liquid fuel rocket engines.

During the summer of 1932 a representative of the German Army Ordnance witnessed a liquid rocket engine test at a site near Berlin. The German Army Ordnance was impressed by these tests. Peace agreements had made no mention of rockets. Von Braun himself was engaged to continue this work, which the then Captain Dornberger directed. At this time von Braun was working toward his doctorate.

Previously Dr. Dornberger had been involved in the development of solid rockets but now the army work was also to include liquid rockets. According to Dornberger himself, the task at this rocket site was to develop a liquid fuel rocket which could be produced by industry and which would have a range greater than any gun. A few years ago, when Dornberger was in America, he quipped that to state the same project goals here would require a five hundred page report!

Thus, German Army Ordnance took up its own development of the rocket rather than allow traditional industry development. This approach, unique at its time, was the forerunner of the present modern weapons system concept. On November 1, 1932 Dr. Dornberger, von Braun, and other co-workers started small test stand work at the Berlin suburb of Kummersdorf. In the next year the Kummersdorf test site was enlarged and received the official name Versuchstelle West (Test Ground West). By the end of 1935 this facility had become much too small for developments, since the German Air Force had also expressed interest in developing rocket propulsion for aircraft. From November 1932 to April 1937 the personnel at Kummersdorf expanded from a mere handful of men to over eighty. In 1931 von Braun graduated from the Institute of Technology at Zurich, Switzerland. In 1932 he obtained his bachelor of science degree from the Institute of Technology at

Berlin. In 1934 he obtained his Ph.D. at the University of Berlin.

At the end of 1935 the German government decided to build a common rocket test site for the Army and Air Force. Peenemünde, on the Baltic coast, was purchased for a common test site. In the summer of 1936 a small detachment of military and technical personnel arrived. Test facilities and personnel were finally moved into the area in April 1937 and Peenemünde was divided into two areas. The Army occupied Proving Ground East while the Air Force occupied Proving Ground West.

Peenemünde, the birthplace of the V-2, thus represented the combined efforts of both the Army and Air Force. A handful of four officers with a staff of 20 administered the 20 square mile area which had a peak employment of 18,000. Thus, Peenemünde was organized as a government-sponsored private research institute which was also capable of producing its own ideas. The budget was on a carte-blanche basis. The head, Dornberger, was responsible only to the chief of the German Army. It is estimated that over-all operating expenses at this facility ran from 1-2 billion reichsmarks (at this time the reichsmark was worth about 45½ cents). The first rocket was the A-1, while the A-2 was launched in 1934 and reached an altitude of over 6,000 ft. from its 670 lb. thrust liquid oxygen–alcohol rocket engine. Four years later the A-3 rocket was powered by a 3,300 lb. engine. In 1939, the A-5 had been developed. In addition, an assist takeoff rocket engine of 2,200 lb. thrust was being developed and was completed by 1942.

In 1939 work began to be concentrated on the A-4 rocket, commonly known as the V-2. Designed to carry a 2,200 lb. warhead to a range of 170-200 miles, the V-2 made its first flight on October 3, 1942. Hitler visited Peenemünde in June 1943 and later ordered the V-2 into mass production. He wanted 30,000 of these rockets to be produced and wanted attacks on

London by October 30, 1943. These massive production goals were never attained. At peak production, only some 30 V-2's could be made per day. The British bombing of the test site on August 17, 1943 did much to cut off further development of the long-range rocket and prompted increased efforts for production. In addition, underground plants were readied for production. First flight of the V-2 against London was made on September 8, 1944 and the last V-2 flight against London was made on March 27, 1945. Some 4,300 V-2's were fired against England and about 2,100 against Antwerp.

Besides the V-2, other German developments included the *Wasserfall* (Waterfall) antiaircraft rocket, the *Taifun* (Typhoon) antiaircraft rocket, and a winged V-2 (the A-4B). This latter rocket made a successful test on January 4, 1945 and it was visualized that it would be placed on top of a larger rocket which would enable warheads to be delivered against the United States from Germany. This winged, step-rocket combination was called the A-9/A-10 Project or more popularly called the "America" rocket. The A-9 was to be a winged version of the V-2. The first stage booster, the A-10, had a design thrust of 440,000 lbs. Beyond this, plans called for the A-11 with a first stage thrust of 3½ million lbs. with the second stage being called the A-10. The A-10 concept is believed to form the basis for present Soviet ICBM's. The A-11, at the present time, would fall somewhere in between our present United States Saturn rocket (with a first stage thrust of 1½ million lbs.) and the Nova rocket (first stage thrust of about 5 million lbs. achieved through a cluster of one million lbs. thrust engines). The Saturn rocket has been fired statically and will be operational around 1962. The Nova rocket is now in the design stage awaiting the development of single chamber engines of one million lbs. thrust.

At the end of the war, the German rocket and space schedule was:

1. Automatic long-range, single-stage rockets (V-2).
2. Automatic long-range gliders (A-9).
3. Manned long-range gliders (A-9B).
4. Automatic multi-stage rockets (A-9/A-10).
5. Manned hypersonic gliders (A-9B/A-10).
6. Unmanned satellites.
7. Manned supply rockets for satellites.
8. Manned satellites.
9. Automatic space vehicles.
10. Manned space vehicles.

Interestingly enough, Soviet missile and space accomplishments seem to have taken this very pattern. The Soviets have even used the same terminology. Thus, items 1, 4, 6, and 9 have already been accomplished and work is believed to have been done on all others. At the close of the war, affairs for the Germans were hectic. At Peenemünde occupants could look forward to either waiting for the Russians to arrive or flee south and be picked up by the Americans. The latter choice was used by some 180 key Peenemünde people including Dornberger, von Braun, and others. However, according to Dornberger, some 4,000 German rocket personnel were captured by the Soviets. The Peenemünde rocket base was taken over by the Russians. In addition, the two underground production facilities in the southern regions of Germany were captured by the Russians. Thus, the Russians were able to utilize to great advantage the existing hardware accomplishments of German rocket technology. They, like the United States, used them to the fullest possible advantage.

German rocket personnel were taken into the Soviet Union but were not actually integrated into the postwar Soviet rocket program. The Russians purposely kept the Germans isolated, picked their brains for what technology they had, did not allow them to mingle with Soviet missile programs, and in the fifties finally allowed them to return to the West. Again, according to

Dornberger, not only did the Russians capture V-2's intact but they also resumed assembly and during the period 1947-1948 they fired hundreds of V-2's for testing and training purposes. The availability of the V-2 is definitely reflected in Soviet Sputnik successes for example. Actual Soviet films show firing and recovering animals in V-2 type vehicles, thus paving the way for Laika in Sputnik II.

Two interesting stories of the work of the captured German scientists have been reported. One is the tale of a top aerodynamicist who was captured in Berlin at the end of 1945. After a few weeks' stay in Germany with his family, he was given these two choices: either go to Siberia or work for the Russians. This professor, along with over two thousand other German engineers and scientists, traveled by rail to Russia during October 22-23, 1946. It is stated that all German scientists were probably moved during those two days. After being deposited in a suburb of Moscow, the professor and the others were put to work on projects given them by the Russians. No contracts or any other agreements were made formally although an informal "submachine gun" contract existed. The scientists were divided into small groups of about fifteen to which were attached about thirty Russian engineers.

Each project was handled by stages. First came the draft stage, then the technical project stage, and finally a presentation stage. Sometimes one German group would be pitted against another to foster a rivalry which would produce the greatest possible improvement in technique.

Whenever a project was virtually completed, it was suddenly canceled and everything pertaining to the work had to be turned in. This point, the Germans felt, was where the real work began—to be done only by an all-Russian group which might be a long distance away. It is stated that each project was followed by a parallel project with an all-Russian group composed of top scientists and financed by unlimited funds.

The Germans were paid about 1500 rubles a month. However, some salaries got up to 5,000 rubles while a few actually received as much as 8,000 rubles. In 1947, however, the salaries of German scientists were cut back very sharply—by half or even more.

The Germans observed that although design and workmanship on civilian goods was primitive and slipshod, the military items were usually of the highest quality. One of the projects mentioned was the coupling of the ramjet and the artillery gun. In the famous November 1957 parade, two huge weapons were actually displayed which were believed to be of the German-developed artillery ramjets.

Although the Germans rated the Russians low on technical imagination, they did show a flair for building military items simply, quickly, and cheaply. Although creative genius such as that of Edison or Diesel does not seem possible in Russian engineers, the Soviets have a tremendous backlog of capabilities. Most engineers, it is stated, know about ten times as much material by heart as the average Western engineer. The reason for this is the Russian's ability to soak up and memorize an immense amount of material primarily because of the wide availability and low cost of textbooks. Indeed, it is further stated that the Russians are a book-reading people. However, it seems that the Soviets themselves have branded their engineers as being too conservative. In 1952 they attempted unsuccessfully to persuade a German aero engineer to stay in Russia voluntarily, under attractive conditions, instead of returning to his homeland.

Later an article in *Pravda* and a broadcast from Radio Moscow both mentioned "stagnated thought" in connection with the engineers. They were accused of using old formulas to solve problems, having a fear of innovation, and making many mistakes in their work. Apparently bureaucracy is heavy in the Soviet Union for the Russian report went on to say that the engineers were burdened with "heaps of paper work" and non-essential routine.

A leading German rocket scientist, Helmut Gröttrup, reported on his experiences in the USSR while working on rocket projects. He tells of similar working conditions. One of his main projects from 1946 to 1950 was Project R-14 (G-4) which was the preliminary design of an intermediate-range ballistic missile. The range was specified as 1,875 miles and was to have the ability to carry a payload of 6,600 pounds. The rocket was to have a thrust of 220,000 lbs. and be generated by the combustion of standard propellants at a combustion pressure of 900 psi. The study showed that it was possible to build a ballistic missile that had a burnout weight which was only 10 per cent of the initial launch weight. Moreover, the payload of this empty "burnout" weight was to be as high as 40 per cent. Initial guidance was via a beam rider system and accuracy of placing the warhead on target was to be 1 per cent of the range and azimuth.

Other details of this German design study carried out for the Soviets indicated that the launch weight was 160,000 lbs. and had a burnout weight (with payload) of 15,400 lbs. The base diameter was on the order of 10-15 ft. and a total length of 80-90 ft. was visualized. It is believed that the design studies on the Soviet IRBM were frozen shortly after 1950-1952. It is to be realized that at this time the Germans had terminated their work for the Soviets. Also, at this time adequate numbers of scientists and engineers, production facilities, and test facilities were available for an all-Soviet program. It took about five years for the Reds to design, build, and test their IRBM which became operational in 1957.

It has been stated that the Germans carried further their work on the previously mentioned A-10 rocket project. Using an A-9 type rocket as an upper stage, the 3,500 mile range rocket was to have a launch weight of 190,000 lbs. Two of the

Germans who worked on this project were Dr. W. Tellman and Professor von Brock. These two are reported to have escaped from Russia in 1949 and are now living in Argentina. The director of this particular project was Professor Artakinov who took over as Soviet director of Peenemünde.

The Soviets are reported to have increased the payload capabilities of the German V-2 by 40 per cent. Peenemünde was then the development center. Whether the report that the Soviets were able to produce 2,000 improved V-2's per month is true is unknown. However, it is sure that they did use the V-2 early in their postwar rocket efforts.

Early in postwar Russia, a large rocket complex was established at Chimki in the suburbs of Moscow and was designated as Works No. 465. Many Germans worked here in the 1½ square kilometer factory. It had five work bays, each 200 meters long. Large structural and tankage rocket problems were worked out here. The Germans reported that work on the "A" Projects (as the rocket program was designated) was also being carried out at Tomsk, Smolensk, Kalinin, Irkutsk, and other places.

American Influence

The GALCIT rocket research project in the United States was informally initiated in 1936 at the California Institute of Technology with the full encouragement of Dr. Theodore von Karman as director. Throughout the next two years a theoretical and practical research program was primarily directed toward the design of a high altitude sounding rocket. The program led to publication of several reports and preparation of a number of others for aircraft companies and government agencies.

In December 1939 General H. H. Arnold, commanding general of the Army Air Corps, requested sponsorship of a program for several problems of vital interest. One of these problems was the development of rockets suitable for boosting airplanes. The rocket problems were chosen by Caltech. The Army Air Corps Jet Propulsion Research Project sponsored by the National Academy of Science got under way at CIT on July 1, 1939. A year later, July 1940, the Army Air Corps assumed sponsorship of the project. In January 1944 the Ordnance Department of the United States Army started to participate in this research program and on November 1, 1944 the project became known as the Jet Propulsion Laboratory, GALCIT. The JPL was formed near Pasadena, California. By 1946 it had 385 employees, and its facilities and equipment were valued at about $3 million. Another agency, the Office of Scientific Research and Development, along with the National Defense Research Committee was also active and spent about $100 million on rocket projects. Its major efforts were for development and production of small caliber artillery rockets. In 1943 the Navy established the U.S. Naval Ordnance Test Station at China Lake, Inyokern, California. Over $100 million in initial investment developed the station which encompassed over 1,000 square miles of area.

The largest and most spectacular rocket missile developed during the war was the WAC Corporal which was tested in the fall of 1945. It was the purpose of this high altitude rocket to carry 25 pounds of meteorological equipment to an altitude of at least 100,000 ft. or almost 19 miles. Firing tests of the WAC Corporal were carried out at the White Sands Proving Ground, Las Cruces, New Mexico, between September 26 and October 25, 1945. The missile reached an altitude of about 43½ miles in vertical flight.

The United States was able to bring completed or salvaged sections of the V-2 back from Germany and these were available for test purposes. In 1946 the Army Air Corps began assessment of the German V-1 and V-2 programs and revealed the limitations of these missiles. This, however, stimulated the Air Force missile research and development. In the same year, under Army Air sponsorship the Rand Corporation undertook studies of earth satellites. Realizing the need for large thrust liquid rocket motors, industrial development of these motors was undertaken in the same year. The motors on which development then started were later to be used in the Redstone, Navaho, Atlas, Thor, and Jupiter missiles. Also, in 1946 the air materiel commander inaugurated Project MX-774 for the purpose of studying rocket missile capabilities with the development of an ICBM rocket as a final objective. Convair produced feasibility and design studies which later led to the birth of the Atlas. However, the contract was canceled later in the year.

It was not until 1952 that the Atlas ICBM component development program was initiated. In 1953 it was reported to the USAF chief of staff that thermonuclear weapons of small weight and size could be produced, thus opening the way to attractive missile payloads. At the same time the Air Research and Development Command placed a contract with the Ramo-Wooldridge Corporation for long-range analytical studies of weapons systems. By 1954 the Air Force Ballistic Missile Division (AFBMD) was activated and was charged with responsibility for management of the research, development, and testing of the Atlas.

In 1955 United States ballistic missile efforts began to take shape. Authority was granted AFBMD to develop the Titan ICBM. President Eisenhower then directed that the ICBM be given the highest priority. AFBMD was instructed to develop the Thor IRBM.

At the same time the Army was engaged in research, development, and production of the Redstone short-range missile and the Jupiter IRBM. This was a parallel program directed by Wernher von Braun. In 1957, some thirteen months after the Air Force Thor contract award, a flight test program began.

Also that year, the first Atlas flight test was made. The Air Force was directed to proceed with deployment of both the Thor and Jupiter IRBM.

Russian Influence

In 1945 the Russians found themselves in Berlin, linked up with the Western powers and the unconditional defeat of Nazi Germany. In addition, the Soviets had occupied a half million square miles of eastern Europe and had annexed a present-day population of 110 million people. Today seven states of western Europe, supposedly independent, are known as satellites of the Soviet Union.

It is said that Stalin himself was one of the first to recognize the significance of coupling a nuclear warhead with a long-range rocket. One particular project that seemed to have caught Stalin's eye was the Sänger concept of the antipodal rocket bomber. This Sänger concept was essentially a winged rocket which could be launched by a large booster rocket. The winged rocket would enter outer space and then by a series of entries and skipping-off tactics, its range would be measured in tens of thousands of miles. It is interesting to note that the present United States Dyna-Soar project which is still several years off from the flying phase stems from this very concept.

At the end of the war Sänger fled from Austria to France. Stalin sent his son Vasily on a mission to Paris to attempt to lure the German rocket pioneer to Russia. However, Vasily was diverted from his purpose into more congenial activities. Apparently like many a rocket project he failed because of technical problems with liquid propellants (cognac) and guidance (French females)! At any rate, Sänger was never brought into the Soviet fold.

In 1947, however, P.N. Kuleshov, general of the artillery, spoke of the great future for long-range rocket artillery. Soviet admirals also spoke of the great possibility of mating the submarine and the rocket and thus being able to strike the heartland of any "capitalistic" nation.

In the early fifties Marshal Pavel Zhigarev, chief of the Soviet Air Force, issued a policy paper where he spoke very highly of the long-range ballistic missile. Zhigarev stated that the ICBM would be the ultimate weapon. In any future war, bomber cemeteries would dot the map, said Zhigarev. This was a reference to Soviet "indignation" at being surrounded by United States bomber bases. Thus the Soviets were early to realize the potential of the ballistic missile. Because of the strong interest at the very top, decisions to enter the missile and space areas were made with a firm hand.

An important aspect of the Soviet influence is to be found in their educational system. It must be realized that the prime function of the Soviet citizen is to serve the state rather than the individual. American education, on the other hand, is designed to bring out the full capabilities of the individual.

The three major philosophical premises of Soviet education are:

1. Advancement of science and technology through central planning of education and research.

2. Scientific and educational efforts are means for advancement of the social economies, and political, and military interests of the nation.

3. The basic truths of human life, nature, and the universe, of social and political and economic reality are beyond debate and it is unnecessary to seek alternative truths.

The school structure is built on four levels. At the preschool level we have the crèches with an age range of a few months to three years. Nursery schools carry the level from three to seven years of age.

In the elementary and secondary levels there are three types of schools. The first is the complete secondary school, which is a ten-year school. Elementary grades are 1-4, intermediate 5-7, and upper grades are 8-10. There are equivalents and alternatives, however, to the elementary and secondary schools. These are: adult evening schools for the elimination of illiteracy, adult schools of the first level, and additional schools of the second level (preparatory training and workers' facilities). In addition there are secondary semiprofessional, trade, and other vocational schools which serve to train semiprofessional skilled labor, the military, and workers for the party.

For higher education there is the regular university plus the more advanced establishments for training the military, security police, party members, managerial personnel, and the postwar-initiated Higher Party School.

Beyond this are advanced training centers.

Elementary and secondary education takes about ten years and covers the ages from seven to seventeen. Students attend school six days a week on a forty hour a week basis in the ten-year program. Teachers are in a privileged category and apparently there is no teacher shortage. It is interesting to note that over the past twenty-five years approximately 1 billion copies of textbooks have been printed. Most of these books have remained unaltered in content for almost twenty years. This is primarily true in the fields of chemistry, physics, and mathematics.

A quota system is used by the Soviet to determine how many people shall be allocated to any given field of work. Methods used to make certain that a specific area will be filled are:

1. Adjustment of the size of student stipend or scholarship.
2. Fixing actual curriculum quotas in various fields.
3. Basing stipends on the quality of the student's work.
4. Subsidization of vacation at student health resorts.
5. Lowering admission requirements.
6. Deferring students from draft (which is required for all eighteen-year-olds).

There are some five major branches of Soviet schools of higher education. These are: engineering-industrial, agricultural, socio-economic, education, and health.

There are four distinct phases of advanced degree training:

1. Aspirantura training, which must be taken by all those who start in the fields of teaching or in scientific research.

2. A candidate degree is awarded to a person who completes Aspirantura and passes oral examinations or writes and defends a thesis. It is also awarded to assistant professors and scientific research associates without going through formal Aspirantura training.

3. Doktorantura training is taken by those holding a candidate degree and desiring to prepare for a doctorate in higher education or scientific research.

4. A doktor degree is awarded to those having a candidate degree or the rank of professor but no candidate degree.

It is estimated by the Soviet planners that on the basis of 100 acceptances in the engineering or scientific fields (with over five years of study) the graduation rate is about 45. In other fields of study it is about 60 graduates per 100 acceptances.

The last stage in Soviet professional training is diploma work for which no degree is awarded. Such work reflects the student's knowledge of his specialty and demonstrates the ability to cope with a research examination. The student ends his university education with oral public examinations before a professor appointed by the Ministry of Higher Education.

Speaking at an engineers' group in Philadelphia, Pennsylvania, H.W. Paige, general manager of the General Electric Missile and Space Vehicle Department on February 20, 1960 gave the following picture of Soviet technical strength:

1. From 1950-1960, the USSR graduated 1.2 million scientists and engineers compared to the United States 0.9 million.

2. In 1959, the USSR graduated 106,000 engineers while the United States figure was 37,000.

3. Women play a vital role in USSR technology: 69 per cent of all medical students in the USSR are women (5.5 per cent for the USA); 39 per cent of all USSR engineering students are women (less than 1 per cent for the USA).

Although the USA leads in total numbers of higher education, it is evident that the USSR is concentrating in the sciences and engineering while the United States entries are concentrating in other "easier" areas. For example, the percentage breakdown of graduations by field of study is shown in the following table:

	USSR %	USA %
Engineering-all types	30.6	7.8
Agriculture	10.4	3.3
Health and medical science	13.9	7.5
All other fields	45.1	81.4
	100.0	100.0

Soviet secondary education is much more concentrated and gives little freedom of choice. For example, Russian students start when they are seven and complete 10 grades and 10,742 hours of instruction by the time they are seventeen. They spend 46.9 per cent of their time in the humanities, 42.4 per cent in sciences and technology, and 10.7 per cent in other training.

As yet there are no studies available on Soviet education for the rocket and space field. Probably none can be made. Even in the United States, education for the space effort is largely conventional (standard sciences and engineering) with on-the-job experience constituting the most important educational area.

The Center of International Studies of the Massachusetts Institute of Technology under Dr. Leon Trilling has studied the Soviet aeronautical engineer. From these studies we may surmise how the Soviet rocket man (or woman!) is trained. The productive goal of the USSR is vested within a small group of powerful ministries. Each determines how many people it will need in the technical areas.

A typical aero student goes through his 55 hour a week study program for five years and receives a 400 ruble per month stipend. He is lucky, however, for only one out of 12 applicants at the Moscow Aeronautical Institute, for example, is admitted. The program is heavy in text materials and some time is devoted to on-the-job training at nearby factories. The overriding feeling that most Westerners (including those Germans who worked for the Reds) have of Russian aeronautical engineers is that they are heavy on theory and prone to solve problems via formulas in books rather than by experimenting. Also, Soviet engineers have decisions and choices made for them— they are so afraid of failure. "Do as you are told and work by the book" seems to sum up the lot of the Soviet engineer.

However, the difference between a captive Soviet technologist and a free American is not the deciding factor, according to United States Vice Admiral Hyman G. Rickover. The contest is not between the free and the enslaved but really which bureaucracy is more efficient. An advantage is seen in the concentration of the Soviet system. This is why the Soviets lead in the present space race—they have made it a matter of national policy to be leaders in this new area of human activity.

And, according to Dr. Eberhardt Rechtin of the Jet Propulsion Laboratory, we are in a space race at the present time; however, at our present rate, we seem forced to be the straight man for Russian space accomplishments.

More material on how the educated Soviet is being implemented into the research and development programs of rockets and space flight will be found in the next chapter, devoted to the organization of research, production, and military establishments which are the cogent factors in Soviet space technology.

CHAPTER 3

THE ORGANIZATION

GEOPOLITICS—the dynamics of a state in a physical world—
is an important variable in assessing the Soviet rocket machine
and its purpose of pushing out into space. Not only is the USSR
the largest country in the world, but it dominates and occu-
pies the "heartland" position of geopolitical concepts. It has a
land area of 8,650 million square miles or about one-sixth of
the land area of the world. Between two and three times the
size of Australia, Brazil, Canada, China, or the United States,
its land mass stretches from the Baltic to the Pacific over a
distance of 6,000 miles—representing a sun time zone difference
of seven hours.

However, the population figure of the USSR amounts to only
about 200 million people, or only slightly more than the United
States and significantly fewer than China or India. Both geography and politics must be considered before we can look at
the dominant space technology groups, the research organization, and the military groups.

Geography

The land mass of the USSR is mostly one giant plain which
ranges from the Black and Caspian seas in the south to the
Arctic Ocean in the north and which extends from the European
countries on the western borders to the Yenisei River in the

east. In the center of this giant land mass are the Ural Moun-
tains running north and south. Along most of the southern and
eastern borders are mountain ranges. The plains areas west of
the Urals constitute the largest population centers, supply most
of the agricultural commodities, and are known for their mineral deposits such as coal, oil, and iron ore.

With the approach of the Germans to the very gates of Moscow, the Soviets undertook a great dispersion program with the
result that present possible military and strategic targets in the
USSR are well spread out. This is both an advantage and a dis-
advantage. The most critical factor seems to be transportation.
Roads, even to date, are very poorly developed and handle only
4 per cent of the freight traffic. Canals carry 12 per cent. Rail-
roads (which are in effect another military service and are
operated under the Army by uniformed personnel) stretch from
border to border—mostly as branches of the Trans-Siberian
Railroad. North–south rail nets are not well developed. The
railroad is the mainstay of heavy freight and carries about 80
per cent of the traffic. Only recently have the Soviets attempted
to use the airplane (at the present time 4 per cent of the traffic)
for movement of people and freight over this far-flung empire.

The climate of the Soviet Union is her most evident enemy.
The USSR lies too far north for normal favorable development.
It should be remembered that the most northerly portion
lies at 75 degrees north and that the southernmost portion is at
35 degrees north. Thus Russia's climate is more like Canada's
than that of the United States. The winters are cold. Even the
most southerly regions (near Iran, for example) have frost
during the winter. Over 66 per cent of the country has a mean
temperature of 32° F. or below for over 150 days of the year.
More than 75 per cent of the USSR has over 120 days of snow
cover per year while the arctic area has over 240 days of snow
cover per year.

Even the Moscow climate covers quite a range. By about

the middle of October snow starts to fall, and the Moscow River is frozen by mid-November. From November through March, average temperatures are below freezing. Average annual snowfall is about 20 inches. Actual temperatures of −40° F. are not unknown in Moscow. By mid-March the snow starts to melt and by mid-April the Moscow River begins her annual thaw. Spring marks the time for mud and floods and there may be frosts as late as June. Summers are hot and humid. While the average temperature is about 70° F. the thermometer has been known to reach 95° F.

Most of the northern areas are tundra—frozen in the winter and swampy in the warm months. The Siberian winters are no joke. At Yakutsk, average winter temperatures range from −60° to −75° F. (and even lower minimum temperatures have been recorded) while in the summer, maximums of 100° F. have been known. Coldest recorded temperatures are at Verkoyansk where −94° F. was recorded. Thus, the dread of being sent to Siberia is a very real fear for the Soviet citizen. With the passing of the Stalin regime, the Soviets have attempted to induce citizens to populate this forlorn region by offering high salaries and other special privileges.

The over-all precipitation in the country is low. In Siberia the year's precipitation is about 16 inches (and mostly in the form of snow) while in the Ukraine it is 8-24 inches; the Turkestan region is quite arid and has a desert-like 4 inches annually. The wettest spot in the USSR is near Batum on the southeast coast of the Black Sea which gets 100 inches of rain per year.

To the south of the tundra is the taiga or forest region. The forests stretch for 5,000 miles and in area are greater than all of eastern and western Europe combined and this constitutes the greatest forest reserve in all the world. South of the forest regions are the mixed forests, followed by the great open steppes. The forested and true steppes constitute some 20 per cent of the USSR in area and are the dominating agricultural regions.

The prize spot of the USSR is the Crimea, popularly known as the "Soviet Riviera," and this includes Yalta, a conference and vacationland. The subtropical Batum on the Black Sea produces fruits, grapes, tea, and tobacco.

Thus, as the Germans found out during World War II, not only can huge armies be swallowed up in the Soviet vastness, but the weather is a very severe enemy.

Economy

The Soviet economy has been organized on a series of so-called Five-Year Plans. Though remarkable strides have been made in expansion of all phases of the economy, the level is generally behind that of the United States in all categories. However, it should be remembered that the rate of expansion of Soviet economy is greater than that of the United States and that the state (and hence also the military) is the prime bene-factor of this expansion. For this reason it is not always wise to compare a United States and USSR production figure for a particular commodity. Most USSR production is plowed back into the economy, a little cream is taken off for the military, and the residual is fed to the populace.

The Gosplan (State Planning Commission) handles all developments. In 1955 Gosplan was divided into long-range and current bureaus. In addition, the bureau Gostekhnika coordinates science and industry.

Agriculture is highly governmentalized and less than 1 per cent of the land is under private ownership. Principle farms are the kolkhoz (collective) and the sovkhoz (state farm). Smaller collectives were further centralized under the MTS or machine tractor stations.

Some two-thirds of the power generated in the USSR comes

from coal. Oil is another important source. Atomic power plants are also springing up. Hydroelectric power, of course, is also well established.

In addition to coal, oil, natural gas, and iron ore, chromium and manganese are important resources. The USSR is dependent on Hungary for bauxite for aluminum and on Czechoslovakia for uranium.

The Soviet industrial capacity, long geared for war, is catching up with the United States. For example, 1957 steel output was about half that of the United States. Though it has plenty of petroleum and therefore a potential petrochemical power, the USSR has combined and centralized its chemical capacity with that of the eastern satellite nations. Plastics—such as the fluorocarbons needed in atomic energy programs and other synthetic resins used as fuel binders for solid propellant rockets —in particular have come under the scrutiny of Khrushchev, and great increases are sought.

Missile Aspects of World Geography

Although much of the USSR industry is now presumably well entrenched behind the Urals, its population is still mainly centered west of the Urals. This makes the Soviets vulnerable to attack from Europe from aircraft or short-range missiles (such as the English-based Thor IRBM or Italy or Turkey-based Jupiter IRBM's). Neither of these missiles, however, has the range to get to the bulk of Soviet industry. The United States Atlas and Titan ICBM's can get to most major spots. However, the Soviets do not publish maps of their centers so that we must largely guess where possible target areas lie and must even resort to out-and-out espionage of the most risky type to get vital military and strategic target data.

Even with accurate maps and accurate guidance, the 5,500 mile ICBM might, when fired under less than ideal operational conditions, be expected to be off its target by several miles. This might result in as much as 5 miles off target for a 9,000 mile range missile. Thus, the United States would have to resort to area warfare, assuming the use of 5 or possibly 10 megaton warheads. The smaller warheads and possibly greater dispersions of the Polaris (1,200 mile sub-launched missile) and the Minuteman (5,000 mile ICBM) would mean that relatively large numbers of these missiles would have to be used.

The over-the-Pole route would be most likely should the United States have to attack the USSR. For this reason, the USSR has constructed an elaborate early warning and tracking system similar to the American-constructed and operated system in Canada. The fact that in 1960 an American RB-47, on a mission to pinpoint Soviet radar tracking sites, was shot down off the coast of the USSR would indicate that the Russian system is operational. The Polaris type of sub may help to change this picture, but the northern approaches (viz., the Arctic Ocean) are ice-covered most of the time.

The recent exploits of the "U.S.S. Nautilus" under the polar ice cap may make prospects somewhat brighter than the long-across-the-flanks attack from either the Pacific or Indian oceans. However, the Polaris type of sub must first find suitable holes in the ice through which to fire its missiles. Not only must it be within range but weather conditions for launch must be suitable. Therefore this time necessary for jockeying into proper position and finding the right weather might give the Soviets a dangerous advantage in the event of war.

The United States is highly vulnerable to submarine missile attacks. Virtually any spot can be reached from the Pacific, Atlantic, or the Gulf of Mexico with an 1800 mile range, sub-launched missile. Of course, all of the United States has an operational early warning and tracking and radar network for aircraft; and for this reason the Soviets may not try to bridge it even with countermeasures. Anyway, most Soviet planes are designed to support ground operations.

The United States is constructing a ballistic missile early warning system (BMEWS) but, at most, it will give us only about a quarter of an hour of warning time. Moreover, it could be saturated by decoys or even completely by-passed. And satellite launching platforms would also offer problems not solved by the system.

What has the climate and geography meant for Soviet missiles? First, the nearest and coldest sites for ICBM's are in the unknown northern regions of Siberia. Thus, when the temperature is −40° F., what does it matter if you handle liquid oxygen (known as LOX) at −180° F. below zero? Moreover, LOX can be made from air. And kerosene or fuel oil would be well suited as a missile fuel since it could also be used to generate power. The hydrocarbons stand up well in the rigors of the arctic. However, big missiles pose a serious problem in above-ground sites in the arctic. Permafrost makes it difficult to support heavy masses. Nevertheless, the Soviets have reported doing considerable work on the installation of heavy structures in the cold regions, both above and below ground. For range purposes it would be wise for the Soviets to put their ICBM bases on the shores of the Arctic Ocean. However, construction techniques in the changeable soil conditions would make for difficult times. Things like structural alignment, power conduits, and propellant service plumbing get difficult to maintain. Therefore, it is more likely that the big bases would be situated further inland, possibly in the more arid or more mountainous regions, even though this would call for increased range on the part of the missiles. Both techniques have likely been attempted.

Then, for mobile army use, the severe climate makes it necessary for extensive protective measures for missile operations. Solid missile performance is especially vulnerable to temperature changes. Some of these missiles, equipped with protective winter heaters, have been seen.

Atomic Energy

Nuclear research is believed to have started long before World War II, under the direction of A.I. Ioffe and D.V. Skobel'tsyn. It is said that in 1927 Commissar N.I. Bukharin offered all the electrical power energy of the city of Leningrad to George Gamow, the famous nuclear scientist now in the United States, in an attempt to initiate a nuclear reaction.

In the spring of 1940 a special committee for the problem of uranium was set up. Headed by V. G. Khlopin, the committee was similar in function to the Briggs Committee set up in the United States in October 1939. From 1941 to October 1943 the demands of war—relocation of science and industry and shortages of trained people—suspended nuclear efforts. Strangely, work was resumed in 1943. It should be recalled that on December 2, 1942, the United States was able to maintain a nuclear chain reaction. Sometime before 1946 or 1947 the Soviets used uranium in a chain reaction. Then developments followed very rapidly. The Soviets exploded their first A-bomb (based on the fission of uranium) in 1949. A Russian hydrogen bomb was detonated in 1953. At Obninsk in the year of 1954, the first Soviet nuclear powered electrical plant went into operation. In Geneva in 1955 and in 1958, the Soviets released a lot of information regarding nonmilitary applications. Also *Atomnaya Energiya* publishes material on nuclear technology on a regular basis. We have found that Soviet reactor types, for example, are similar in design to those in the United States. On the other hand, nuclear energy is being exploited on the basis of long-term benefits through technology rather than on any economic basis.

The nuclear rocket program is tied into space technology very neatly. Advisers like the noted nuclear scientist, Peter L. Kapitsa, help the USSR Academy of Sciences and its space sub-group, the Astronautical Commission, on such vital areas as cryogenics (the area of very low temperatures). Kapitsa has made many contributions to the cryogenics field and his work on liquid hydrogen is among them. Liquid hydrogen is looked on as one of the ultimate chemical fuels and it also makes a good working fluid for use in the nuclear rocket. Some of Kapitsa's work has even helped the United States missile effort. For example, the Kapitsa process of liquefying air using a low-pressure cycle, and a turboexpander has been utilized in a van-mounted, mobile military LOX plant; a weight reduction of 75 per cent was achieved in terms of weight per ton of product.

The Academy of Science, however, has a rather tight hand on the entire nuclear energy program and runs the USSR Institute for Atomic Energy; the IAE is a scientific group governed by scientists.

Political Aspects

The USSR was formed in 1922 and the constitution was adopted in 1936 even though the czarist regime was overthrown by the Russian Revolution of 1917. Today the total constituent republics amount to fifteen. The ultimate state body is the Supreme Soviet and it has two sections—the Soviet of the Union (a group similar to our House of Representatives) which is based on one deputy per 300,000 people, and the Soviet of Nationalities, with delegates elected according to nationality. Deputies serving are:

  25 from each constituent republic
  11 from each autonomous republic
   5 from each oblast or section
   1 from each okrug or smaller division

A presidium acts for the Supreme Soviet when it is not in session. The Supreme Soviet also appoints the Council of Ministers.

Needless to say, the Communist party is the only legal political group in the USSR.

Other Soviet governmental groups include krays, or large sections of land situated at some distance from the center of Russia. The kray comprises the self-governing oblast, the oblast administered by the central government, and the smaller okrug, as well as the rayon or small economic-administrative district which is divided into rural or urban Soviets.

The Research Scene

In any analysis of present or future Soviet rocket developments, one should take into account the tremendous research efforts now being sanctioned by the government. This research, coupled with an already vast and yet growing hardware capability, allows us to catch a sometimes shadowy glimpse of the road that present and future rockets are taking. Because the Soviets freely publish their long-range goals, we can be fairly certain of their direction but we cannot know their exact timetable or details of the mechanisms of implementation. Hardware details, moreover, are traditionally kept secret often long after a particular item is obsolete.

Today's research can be said to be the breeding ground for future Red efforts in space. All USSR research is under the direction of the Academy of Science, headed by Dr. Alexander N. Nesmeyanov. This powerful group originates all research—whether it be classified or unclassified—that the nation is to carry out. The academy has divisions in the following areas: biology, chemistry, geography, geology, physics, technology, and the nonphysical sciences such as economics, history, linguistics, the literary field, and philosophy. There is apparently little duplication of research effort because of the central position of the academy. And there is no such thing as "private" research.

First, the leaders of all the sciences—and there are some five hundred such leaders—the topnotch men, set the sights for all work and effort. Assignments—whether they be military or non-military—are handed out to the various groups for implementation.

Second, the academy also knows what is going on in technical areas outside the country. The Institute of Scientific Information makes it a point to obtain and review about 8,000 scientific journals of the world (some 1,400 are from the United States and about 800 are from Britain). Abstracts are made available to scientists. The institute also publishes *Vaprosy Raketnoi Tekhniki* ("Problems of Rocket Technology"); this publication provides translations and surveys all rocket literature. The main publication of the institute, however, is the *Referativanyi Zhurnal* ("Abstract Journal").

The recently established Siberian branch of the Academy of Science has issued a new journal of direct interest in the fields of combustion and rocketry. The new journal is *Kinetika i Kataliz* ("Kinetics and Catalysis").

However, all is not well with the Soviet scientific and information program. Recently, Professor A. I. Mikhaylov, institute director of the All Union Institute of Scientific and Technical Information was given the task of streamlining the program. It was charged that the *Referativanyi Zhurnal* did not cover such vital areas as medicine, transportation, agriculture, light, and the food industries. Moreover, there was said to be a great delay in issuing necessary indexes and that too much time elapsed between receipt of the publication for abstracting and the availability of the abstract to the user. It was also charged that the circulation was far too small.

In addition to the journal, the All Union Institute issues technical literature aids such as *Igoti Nauki* ("Achievements of Science"), a monograph series; and the *Ekspress-informatsiya* ("Express Information").

The literature problem remains a difficulty. However, the

Soviets do glean a lot from the rest of the world. About 50 per cent of the scientific journals are in English, 16 per cent in Russian, 12 per cent in German, 10 per cent in Japanese, and the rest are in the various other languages of the world.

However, only 7 per cent of American scientists read Russian whereas 70 per cent of the Russian professionals read English.

The Soviet information bureau has a staff of over 50,000 scientists, engineers, translators, and librarians; 14,000 are paid for full-time work. Publications are received from 95 countries (written in 65 languages) and each day, the Soviets scan, translate, catalogue, and distribute from 2,500 to 3,000 technical articles.

The Soviets apparently do not respect copyright or even author's usual rights. According to George Sutton, his book *Rocket Propulsion Elements* was translated into Russian and widely distributed; for this he did not receive a red ruble or even a red cent! Portions of this author's book on solid rockets have been seen in Russian publications without author source being mentioned. Even these seem insignificant compared with recent tactics. Lockheed Missile published a highly technical book on magnetohydrodynamics. Within weeks it was published in Russian. The situation sometimes becomes ridiculous. One scientist anxiously awaited the arrival of a Russian report dealing with his specialty. When it arrived it turned out to be a retranslation of the scientist's own paper that he had written some months previous!

How can one keep up with Soviet space developments? Unfortunately there is no one source that covers all fields. Two very good general sources are published by the United States Government and are available to all on a subscription basis. The Office of Technical Services, Business and Defense Services Administration, U.S. Department of Commerce, issues its *Technical Translations* twice a month. It gives abstracts in a wide variety of fields and includes: astronomy, atmospheric physics, ordnance, missiles, satellite vehicles, engines and propulsion systems, fuels, electronics, and nuclear technology. It also tells where to get copies of the translated papers or books. Most of the items abstracted are from Soviet periodicals, but the satellite nations and some other countries (like Red China, for example) are also covered. Annual subscription is $12 per year.

The U.S. Central Intelligence Agency publishes its semi-monthly *Scientific Information Report* and usually gives more detailed selected abstracts of unevaluated information extracted from recently received publications of the USSR, eastern Europe, and Red China. Areas of rocket interest covered are: fuels and propellants, industrial chemistry, nuclear fuels, electronics, engineering, and physics. Cost is $28 per year.

Yet another source is the recently initiated "Russian Supplement" published regularly in the *ARS Journal*. Under National Science Foundation subsidy, selected Soviet articles specifically in the fields of rocketry and space flight are published.

Rocket Reviews is published by the author each month and covers both Soviet and United States rocket and space literature in abstract form.

All of these sources have one major shortcoming. This is the delay in time between receipt of paper, translation or review, and publication. Delays range from several months to several years.

We don't know how much the USSR is actually spending on research but it is probably a lot. However, even science has inflationary trends for on December 20, 1957 Dr. Nesmeyanov spoke before the Soviet Council of the Union and asked for a boost in research spending. No over-all figure was given, however. In 1958 Jozif Kuzmin (the first deputy premier and head of the state planning commission) said that the USSR would spend 18.2 billion rubles (about $5 billion) just for "developing science" and something like $72½ million for a new research center in Siberia. It is hard to weigh these figures. They might include military research, or they may be incomplete for security reasons. However, we do feel that the Soviets are supporting scientific research to the greatest possible extent.

What is the status of the Soviet technical man? He is far better off than the factory worker and ranks high on pay scales. A starting Soviet scientist (say the equivalent of a B.S.) earns from two to three times the salary of a factory worker, while top Academy of Science personnel may draw ten times the amount of an ordinary worker.

Academician A. A. Blaganravov, a key Soviet rocket man, for example, gets 13,000 rubles per month just for being on the presidium of the academy. In addition, he obtains a regular salary from a research institute. It is estimated that this particular rocket man, for example, earns a total of 20,000 to 25,000 rubles per month. The official ruble exchange rate is set at four per dollar; however on the open market, the ruble is valued at around ten cents. Nevertheless, scientists are still highly paid even if one takes the unfavorable rate.

Scientists enjoy other privileges that the factory worker could not hope to obtain. Scarce items like automobiles, television, and hi-fi sets, country places at resorts, servants, and travel allowances make it evident that the Soviets are using material incentives that would challenge capitalistic techniques.

Further, the Soviets have adopted a unique reward system for patents and the like. For any patent which will net the state an income of 9 million rubles per year, the inventor gets a nice lump sum payment of 200,000 rubles. For what are merely termed "technical improvements," lump sum payments of 100,-000 rubles have been claimed.

Even further, the USSR is grinding out more scientists, engineers, and technicians than the United States and is providing adequate research facilities which are stocked with the best of Soviet equipment.

Recently, the USSR Academy of Science formed a Commission on Interplanetary Communications (space flight). L.I. Sedov is president (Sedov is now also serving as president of the International Astronautical Federation) while G. Karpenko acts as secretary. The famous nuclear scientist, Peter Kapitsa, is said to be an adviser; and the direct responsibility for the launching of the Sputniks is attributed to this group. Space flight is thus an official function of the USSR policy. This is borne out by Khrushchev's own words, lauding space shots to the fullest propaganda advantage, and finally permitting top Soviet rocket scientists to roam in the free world.

Another indication of the official government sanction given to space flight is the establishment of the Ziolkovsky Gold Medal as announced by the presidium of the USSR Academy of Science. This honor "will be awarded to Soviet and foreign scientists for original work of major significance in the development of astronautics." The first period was from 1950 to 1956 and was to be covered by an award in 1957. Thenceforth, the medal was to be awarded every three years. The first prize went to those responsible for orbiting the first Sputnik.

The rocket and satellite activity between the academy and the military hardware groups of the services filters through the Chakalov Central Aero Club, the Russian counterpart of our American Rocket Society, and the Institute of Aeronautical Sciences. Several years ago, this club formed an astronautics section. Technical committees of the Moscow section, for example, are: rocket technology, radio telecontrol, and space medicine.

Astronautical voice in the USSR has always been active and recently associated with the same general freedom connected with the basic sciences. Prior to Sputnik, not much attention was given to the Soviet writings on space flight. Yet, looking back on them, they all pointed to the Soviet space accomplishments of today—the first satellite, living beings in orbit, velocities needed for space probes, lunar trajectories, etc. Not only did these works become more voluminous, but the USSR in 1956 ended its rocket silence when a delegation of scientists attended the First International Congress on Rockets and Guided Missiles in Paris to describe animal-carrying rocket tests.

A year later, the dog Laika was in orbit. The thirteen-man delegation was headed by Comrade (though as we have seen he is a capitalist as far as payroll is concerned) A. A. Blaganravov, member of the presidium of the Academy of Science and, incidentally, an armaments expert. A prelude to a liberal opening up of the rocket sciences was provided in August 1955 when Sedov and Ogorodnikov visited the Sixth International Astronautical Congress in Copenhagen. In 1956 the USSR made formal application for membership in the IAF (International Astronautical Federation). This was followed by attendances at an international symposium at Yale University, the Ninth International Congress of Applied Mechanics in Brussels, and the Seventh International Astronautical Congress in Barcelona. L. Sedov, an expert in hydrodynamics, was elected a vice president at the latter meeting in 1957.

Incidentally, Blaganravov and Sedov headed a Soviet delegation at the all-American ARS meeting in Washington, D.C., in November 1959. It is reported that Sedov, when he saw the ninety foot long Titan ICBM on display in front of the Sheraton Park Hotel quipped, "To what scale is this missile?"

Just when the astronautical scene started to get friendly, the U-2 incident came along. Soviet astronautics was quick to cool down with the official party line which resulted, as is known, in the collapse of the Summit meeting. Politics has come to be injected into astronautics, also. At the Eleventh International Astronautical Congress in Stockholm in August 1960, president of the IAF Sedov made attempts to give absolute veto power to both the United States and the USSR in the twenty-nine nation group. Sedov also wanted a guarantee that both the United States and USSR would be in the top officership each year. In addition, the Soviets declined to participate in two new IAF ventures: an International Astronautics Academy, and an International Institute of Space Law.

Although there appears to be some political rift between Moscow and Peking, Red Chinese research is following the Soviet research pattern. During 1960 Andrew G. Haley, well-known observer of the international rocket picture, published his views on the activities of Red Chinese research; and the People's Republic of China established a Chinese Academy of Sciences staffed by top scientists.

By the end of 1958 Red China had over 840 natural and technical science research institutions with over 32,000 research workers. The Science Press of the Academia Sinica published 2,050 books and 2,700 periodical issues in the period 1950-1959. As in the USSR, an Institute of Scientific and Technical Information has been set up and it publishes 89 literature aids.

In 1956 Chairman Mao Tse-tung asked scientific workers to advance their levels and a twelve-year plan was initiated for the development of science and technology; guidance for the entire program was to be monitored by the State Council. A great coup for Red China research was scored in 1953 when the Chinese-American, H.S. Tsien, returned to Red China. Dr. Tsien had for many years been a leader in America in the advancement of jet propulsion, rockets, and astronautics. He was Robert H. Goddard Professor of Jet Propulsion at the California Institute of Technology. Now Dr. Tsien is a director of the Academia Sinica (Peking), Institute of Mechanics.

It is Mr. Haley's belief that Dr. Tsien is a leader in Red China's efforts to bring the rocket back to China where it probably originated. As it may be recalled, the rocket was first mentioned in world literature in the Sung Dynasty (eleventh century) and it is generally believed that the Chinese invented or stumbled onto the rocket principle long before anyone in

the Western world. There have been reports also that the
Chinese are equipped with smaller field or artillery rockets.
These are likely of Soviet surplus vintage. Probably the Chinese
are also carrying on rocket development of their own. The Soviet
T-7A, for example, has been openly displayed by the Red
Chinese.

Other satellite nations are known to be involved in rocket
work. Polish universities are working with high altitude rocket
soundings of the earth's atmosphere. A Warsaw institute
published pictures of rockets that look like the T-7A and the
M-100A, both Soviet solid rockets. Albania has also displayed
heavy Soviet rockets. Czechoslovakia, Hungary, and Rumania
have published reports on various research phases of the space
program. It is apparent, then, that the Soviets, under a
centralized command, have "farmed out" a number of basic
space flight problem areas to the satellites. However, little if
any rocket or space activity has been evidenced by the East
German Democratic Republic (East Germany).

The fullest possible means of exploiting these research efforts
have not been overlooked. The USSR and the satellite nations,
for example, were quick to utilize the postage stamp as a means
of carrying their achievements to the world. Issuance of a
Ziolkovsky commemorative stamp almost coincided with the
launching of Sputnik I. Lenin is pictured with a rising rocket.
Czechoslovakia has a stamp that illustrates the carrier rocket
of Sputnik II. Rumania showed a detailed view of the "Laika"
orbital dog equipment. A Mongolian stamp showed the other
side of the moon shortly after the Soviets officially released their
photos. There has been such a consistent pattern of these stamp
issues so soon after the event that one would think that it had
been planned that way! With the billions of dollars the United
States has put into the rocket and space program, only once
has it issued a stamp of a rocket—and that was a German V-2!

On stamps the Soviets picture themselves as dynamically using rockets for peaceful purposes.

Research Projects

The USSR formally participated in the International Geophysical Year. A vital part of this IGY work centered around rocket and satellite experiments. Sputniks I, II, and III are well known; however, much more work-horse research took place for the IGY. The Soviets announced at the beginning that they would fire about 125 rockets in all during the IGY.

In a letter to CSAGI at Brussels, Academician I.P. Bardin (vice president of the USSR Academy of Science and president of the USSR National IGY Committee) gave the following study goals for Soviet satellite and upper atmosphere rockets:

structural parameters of the atmosphere
optical properties of the atmosphere
ultraviolet and solar x-ray radiation
solar corpuscular radiation and aurorae
cosmic radiation
ionospheric phenomena
the magnetic field of the earth
micrometeorites and meteorites
the chemical and physical processes in the upper layers
    of the atmosphere

So-called "container" techniques were utilized for experiments at altitudes of up to 125 miles. The instrumented containers were detached from the rocket a certain time after rocket engine firing. Some data were telemetered back while instruments were returned to the earth for examination. Distribution of rocket firings by zones and years were:

Zone 1. The Arctic. Franz Josef Land, 80°N, 1958: 25 firings
Zone 2. The Middle USSR Latitudes, 50°-60°N, 1957: 30
    firings, 1958: 40 firings

Zone 3. The Antarctic (Mirny), 50°60° S, 1957-1958: 30
   firings

Firings of rockets and satellites took place at approximately
even intervals throughout the IGY, mainly on World Days, or
on occasions of active solar elements, that is, on Special
World Days. Much data has lately been published. Much, however, remains to be published. Details of carrier rockets have
not been given. These ambitious programs and tests did indicate
that a large number of rockets were available for research
purposes.

Not long ago the Soviets gave us a first glimpse of their new
scientific research ship, the "Shokalsky," a 3,600 ton vessel,
equipped to fire meteorological rockets. The ship can remain at
sea for 120 days and has a top speed of 13 miles per hour. The
rockets, about 12 inches in diameter and over 15 feet long
(propulsion system is unknown) are stored in the hold of the
ship and fired from a forward deck launching tower. The instrumented rockets can attain altitudes of 50 miles and give
data on temperature, pressure, and radiation in the upper
atmosphere. Many of these rockets have been fired from this
ship in the vicinity of Soviet Mirny located in the antarctic and
in the equatorial waters and northern waters of the Pacific
Ocean. Home base for the rocket-firing ship is Vladivostok.
Other duties of the ship are to measure atmospheric radio-
activity, precipitation, and sea water.

The Military

Without doubt, the military actually holds the key to the vast
number of rockets available not only for military purposes but
also for satellites, high altitude soundings, and for special space
shots.

In the Soviet Union there are only two military services—

the Army and the Navy. The Army is by far the largest and most powerful, but the Navy has moved up fast. The Soviet Army is organized into these separate components:

ground

air

antiair

The Navy is a separate service. In addition, there are minor components such as the security troops, a military force governed by the Ministry of Internal Affairs (MVD) and the Committee for State Security (KGB). All armed forces are controlled by a single high command under the Minister of Defense. Each force is represented in the ministry, but the chain of command passes directly from the Minister of Defense to all major commands at home and on foreign soil.

ARMY

The Soviet Army plays a dominant role in all of the armed forces. For example, during World War II, Soviet air and naval units operated directly in sole support of ground forces. Presently, army commands incorporate both air and ground elements. Principal army commands in peacetime are military districts within the USSR and groups outside Soviet borders. The ground forces are organized into:

armies

corps

divisions (which include nondivisional brigades)

regiments

battalions

During times of war, the field forces are organized tactically into fronts—a term somewhat analogous to the groups of the United States Army during World War II.

At the present time, the over-all strength of the Soviet Army is about 2½ million men organized into about 175 divisions; however, this number can be doubled within thirty days since materiel and cadre to fill out new groups are in a constant state of readiness. The main striking force of the Soviet Army are the 22 divisions of the Group of Forces maintained in East Germany and thoroughly mechanized and armored. In addition, there is available an air-borne force of about 100,000 men. It is interesting to note that the much lauded fleet of Soviet turboprop and turbojet transports stems from military bombers which are noted for long range, have the ability to take off and land in short, unimproved fields, and are readily convertible from commercial to military use. Thus they provide an unusual and almost invulnerable transport system within the Soviet Union and also a possible means of landing combat troops in the United States!

Presently used transports are:

1. The Tu-114 "Russia" turboprop with a capacity of 220 which can fly nonstop from Moscow to any spot on the earth. Cruising speed is 550-560 mph.

2. Tu-104, a 4-engine turbojet which was flying regular schedules a year before the first United States commercial jet flew. It took only 18 months to design, build, and fly this modification of the "Badger" medium jet bomber.

3. The Tu-110 which has a capacity of 100 and can take off from a runway of 5,100 ft. and land in 3,900 ft. Standard NATO runways are 8,000 ft. long.

In addition to being able to transport combat troops, most of these planes could be used to carry small guided missiles or for parachute operations. It would take only 250 Tu-114's to transport about five divisions of light infantry from the USSR to anywhere in the United States in a matter of hours (presumably under the shock blow of an all-out nuclear attack). In the United States, interestingly, we have a strategic reserve of less than four divisions.

In the satellite nations of eastern Europe, there are about 10 Soviet divisions. Within the Soviet Union, there are the remaining 143 divisions (most of these are under-strength), and concentration is in the Far East and on the southern borders. The armies of the satellites and Communist China total more than the Soviet Army but they are not believed to be equivalent in strength and equipment.

Soon after World War II ended, development of the rocket efforts was centralized in a concentrated agency, located in Moscow under the directorship of General A.S. Yakolev. This was called the Office of Special Weapons. During the later years of development, it was felt that the Red Army would have major control over rockets and guided missiles. This development was thus under control of an artillery marshal. As the Minister of Defense has always been an army officer, it was logical that Marshal Mitrofan Ivanovich Nedelin should be named as Soviet rocket chief, thus indicating that the rocket had grown in importance to the point where a separate missile command had to be created. Nedelin's title was said to be Marshal of Rocketry. The new branch of the service was at first considered to be a fourth command, in addition to the Army, Navy, and Air Force; but it is now believed to be under army control along with the air and antiair forces.

Nedelin was born in 1903 or 1904 and joined the Soviet Army after the revolution. In the late twenties, following his graduation from an artillery school, he went on to Dzerzhinsky Artillery Academy from which he received his degree in 1935. From 1936 to 1939 he acted as adviser to the Spanish Loyalists in the Spanish civil war.

When he returned to Russia, Nedelin became a colonel of artillery and was stationed near Moscow. During World War II he organized and commanded artillery units; and he is said to have been responsible for the logistics of artillery operations outside Russian borders. At the end of the war he had the rank of colonel general.

Shortly after the death of Stalin in 1953, Nedelin, who was a member of the Communist party and of the Central Committee, was made a marshal. His ranks have included: Marshal of Artillery; C-in-C, Army Artillery; and Chief of Main Artillery (Ministry of Defense).

This engineer–general was said to control over 100 missile bases and a personnel of about 200,000. In addition, he was reported to be in charge of nuclear warhead factories, guided missile plants, rocket test sites, and guided missile units.

In the United States, missile commands are spread among the three services plus several administrative offices. With such strong central support it is no wonder the Soviets have been able to make a significant reduction in the time between the design concept and operational status of military missiles, and also to provide sufficient extra aircraft for special high-altitude and space missions.

On October 20, 1960, Marshal Nedelin was a victim in an air crash during a tour of Soviet missile bases. Previously, Nedelin had been hailed by Khrushchev as a hero for the shooting down of the U-2 by a Soviet rocket. Khrushchev had called Nedelin "a remarkable soldier, a hero of the Soviet Union, a splendid artillery man who knows more about rocketry than anybody." Funeral services for fifty-eight-year-old Nedelin were held in Red Square and were indicative of his high position.

Marshal Kirill Semenovich Moskalenko, sixty, took over as supreme commander of Soviet missile forces. Moskalenko also had a long-time background in the Soviet military spectrum. Joining the Communist party in 1926, Moskalenko was an infantry division commander during World War II and was credited with breaking the Germans in the Ukraine. Elected as a supreme Soviet deputy in 1954, Moskalenko was made a part of the Central Committee of the party in February 1956. Also during 1956, Moskalenko became a marshal and afterwards had served as chief of the Moscow Military Garrison. This appointment also indicates that the Soviets still continue to place the rocket as a ground-controlled weapon commanded by ground forces.

With the exception of naval and aircraft rockets, all missiles are under the control of the Red Army. Thus, all rockets are considered extensions of artillery and under the jurisdiction of an artillery officer. Small artillery rockets are standard components of infantry divisions. Larger weapons may be attached where necessary.

ROCKET BATTALION OF A TYPICAL MECHANIZED DIVISION[1]

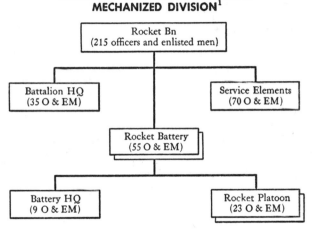

1 7.72 mm. LMG
3 140 mm. Rocket Launchers[2]

[1] The rocket battalion in a tank division has 12 rocket launchers of 240 mm. and a total strength of 230 men.
[2] Principal weapons: 4–7.62 mm. LMG (light machine guns); 12–140 mm. rocket launchers.

Figure 1

Other rockets such as the IRBM, the ICBM, and antiaircraft missiles are believed to be under the new rocket command. Figure 1 illustrates the breakdown of a typical rocket battalion in a mechanized division. Hardware details are given in a later chapter.

The standard tank battalion for the rocket group, composed of 230 officers and men, is equipped with 12 rocket launchers of 240 mm. caliber, mounted on standard trucks. The mechanized division also has its rocket battalion, but it is manned by 215 officers and noncoms with another dozen rocket launchers on standard trucks although the rockets are lighter and of 140 mm. caliber. Going up the scale, each mechanized army is composed of 2 tank divisions, 2 mechanized divisions, an antiaircraft artillery division, an artillery brigade, and a rocket launcher regiment with about 100 rocket launchers.

It is certain that a vast family of missiles was early conceived. The liquid rockets were based on LOX for the most part. Solid rockets were first to utilize double-base propellants but later switched to composites. Cruise missiles were also on the early development list. One source has stated that from 1946 to 1955 the Soviets fired as many as 100,000 small, medium, and large rockets in their development program. In 1955 nuclear weapons were heavy, guidance was primitive, and this meant large rockets (and large thrust) to deliver relatively heavy nuclear weapons. Then, rather than wait for the development of lightweight, high-yield atomic weapons, the Soviets decided to go ahead on a family of long-range weapons and many specialized shorter range vehicles, as well. This is the only reason, as I see it, that the Soviets were able to develop their rocket forces some two to five years ahead of the United States: They just started sooner.

By 1949 or 1950 the Soviets were completely on their own. They built a complex of factories and test installations, and trained thousands of scientists and engineers.

Then came the decision from the top: The hell with this paper work, let's get some hardware. Don't wait for technology to make design work easier, let's get going now. Damn the weight, just give it enough thrust! And the philosophy of the big but simple rocket has paid off handsomely for the Soviets. For one thing, in military weapons they can now either carry bigger warheads than originally planned to the same design range or they have been able to extend the range and keep the same yield of weapon. Secondly, it has paid off in the space area by allowing the orbiting of putting relatively large payloads deep into space.

AIR FORCE

Following World War II, the Soviet Union became a major world air power. Although support of ground operations is still the primary mission of the army-controlled Air Force (about one-half of air strength is devoted to tactical support), USSR air power has been widened to include long-range air arms. The air armies are the largest Soviet operational air units and are designated as either tactical or strategic. In each air army there are normally three corps and each of these has subordinate divisions. These latter contain three regiments. The long-range strategic striking force is under the operational control of the Minister of Defense. The tactical units are controlled directly by the particular military district or commander of a certain segment. Thus, the Soviet Air Force is owned, controlled, and operated by and for the Red Army!

With a fleet of some 20,000 operational aircraft, the air forces of the Soviet Army have these components:

> tactical aviation
> fighter aviation of antiair defense
> aviation of airborne troops
> long-range aviation
> naval aviation

With the exception of long-range aviation, all aviation is subordinate to major commands of the Army and Navy. Some 65 per cent of all aviation is assigned for tactical use.

Soviet aviators are rated high for their physical and mental skills. Air training begins in the paramilitary air clubs, open to youths of over fifteen years of age. On completion of this preliminary training, the youth is eligible to enter the Air Force or the Air Reserve. Some three years are normally put in at a military training school. Theory, demonstration, and training are emphasized.

There are rocket armaments and other special rocket weapons of long-range, medium-range, and short-range bombers for the air force fleet. These are primarily stand-off weapons which allow the aircraft to strike a target while staying out of range of target defenses. Fighters and interceptors are known to be equipped with standard and specialized rockets, also. All of these rockets of importance are described in Chapter 4.

ANTIAIR

The antiair defense forces (usually called PVO) have the over-all responsibility of maintaining defense against air and guided missile attack. The antiair defense forces are broken down into two components—Antiair Defense of the Homeland and the Antiair Defense of the Forces. Homeland defense is the primary mission of the PVO and covers all the centers of populations and industry in the USSR. The commander in chief of PVO has assigned to him a component of the army air forces which is called Fighter Aviation of Air Defense (abbreviated to IAPVO). He has available large numbers of antiaircraft artillery and guided missile units, regiments, and battalions of special signal troops called Air Observation, Report, and Signal Service (known as VNOS). Still other forces assigned to home defense are antiaircraft, searchlight, chemical defense, engineer, and construction units. All of these forces are organized into antiair defense districts which include all the principal possible target complexes of the USSR. All personnel for antiair defense forces are provided by the other forces.

A number of salient features arise when one analyzes Soviet air defense (which has been extended to include guided missile attack). First, civilian defense is a well-organized activity of the Soviet Union. Civilian defense appears to be much better organized and financed than in the United States. Second, the Soviets believe that they can stop any invading United States bombers by means of their rocket-armed interceptors and anti-aircraft guided missiles. The American "spy plane," the U-2, is said to have been shot down by a Soviet guided missile. In his recent book *Countdown for Decision,* General John B. Medaris (former commander of the United States Army Ballistic Missile Agency which was responsible for development of the Redstone and Jupiter, and also for orbiting the first American earth satellite, the Explorer) said there is no reason to doubt the Soviet claim of shooting down our plane at 60,000 ft. In the Moscow military parade of November 7, 1960, the Soviets showed a missile of a type which had been used to shoot down the U-2. The antiaircraft missile is called the Silver Needle; it consists of two stages. A booster rocket with fins was 10-12 ft. long and the second stage had a diameter of about 1 ft. and a length of about 10 ft.

The United States has already demonstrated the practicability of one Nike rocket shooting down another Nike rocket at altitudes far in excess of 60,000 ft. It will be recalled that the mission of the U-2 was an attempt to photograph a Soviet space shot on the pad and also to make a photo run over Sverdlovsk to find antiaircraft guided missile complexes. Vice President Nixon saw dome-shaped complexes there on his visit; and these were said to be antiaircraft missile launching pads. Third, the Soviets use the fact that the United States has "surrounded" the USSR with bomber bases and guided missile pads to keep up the civilian defense effort and further engender hatred for the United States within the Soviet citizenry. Fourth, should it be necessary, the Soviets would be willing to "sacrifice" their population centers and industrial complexes in an atomic holocaust in order to gain world domination.

NAVY

Although the USSR Navy during World War II was almost entirely used for offshore support of ground operations, the Soviets now have a modern long-range striking fleet. The United States acknowledges that the Soviet fleet is second only to the American in size and modernity. The Soviets have two obsolete battleships but surface vessels are mainly concentrated into modern, fast cruisers and destroyers. Most are equipped with radar and some are believed to be armed with guided missiles. Though naval aviation has 3,500 aircraft (50 per cent are jet fighters, 25 per cent are light jet bombers, and the rest are transports, recons, and miscellaneous aircraft), the Red fleet has no aircraft carriers.

The most potent striking force of the Red fleet is the large number of submarines—reported to be in the neighborhood of five hundred. Most have been built since World War II and many are of the long-range "snorkeling" type. Present reports have it that the Soviets plan to launch at least one nuclear sub per month. Between the end of World War II and the emergence of the nuclear sub, the maximum production rate of the conventional sub was said to have been one per week. The Volga-Don Canal was completed in 1953 and is of sufficient size to enable submarines to travel from the Baltic to the Black Sea.

The Soviet merchant fleet ranks eleventh in the world's registry of gross tonnage and fourth in total number of ships. In an effort to aid submarine research and possibly provide knowledge for attack of other countries in the event of war, the Soviet Union is investing deeply in oceanographic research. Many research vessels are now plying the world's oceans. Some of these ships are disguised in the form of commercial vessels. Important missile firings by the United States from

Cape Canaveral and the California coasts are said to have been monitored by Soviet surface and submarine vessels.

While the Soviets have many "snooping" ships in operation, they have even greater plans for the future. Russia is embarking on a construction program calling for two hundred modern trawlers equipped with the latest electronic, radar, and sonar detection equipment. These will be used to increase knowledge of basic oceanographic facts. However, the authoritative American publication, *Underwater Engineering*, reports that the "basic" information now collected by such ships includes: topography of the ocean bottom near our coast, losses of electromagnetic transmissions, temperature and currents, and other acoustic data. All of this information would be needed in the event that the Soviets decided to stage a naval attack on the United States.

It is interesting, also, that the number of Soviet landings on arctic pack ice have been steadily increasing. This is significant in the light of the possible "over-the-Pole" flight of long-range bombers or ballistic missiles against the North American continent. In addition, such temporary installations would also aid the Soviets in setting up their own base lines for bomber or missile attacks against the United States. And yet another possibility looms up: The Soviets could set up an underwater warning system in the arctic which would make for difficult times for our Polaris type of submarine. If this should occur, then the future will see United States submarines being lost while on missions in the Arctic Ocean. As with nearby flying aircraft (even though they may be outside the territorial limits), the Soviets are apt to shoot first.

There are three known types of Soviet submarines. The Z-Class or "guppy" types number around two hundred and are used for long-range torpedo attack and mine-laying purposes; this sub reportedly is capable of carrying solid propellant ballistic missiles. There are about one hundred medium-range attack subs and perhaps two hundred limited-range coastal subs. Details of naval rockets are given in the chapter on hardware.

In addition to surface craft and naval aviation, the Soviet Navy has control of coast defense forces which include naval infantry (Marines), coast artillery, and antiaircraft defense.

In 1959 a Soviet Navy captain, Nikolai Fedorovich Artamonov, defected to the United States. He stated that since the first of 1955 Soviet naval strategy has been predicated on the basis of a surprise and all-out Soviet naval attack on the United States itself. This former officer also confirmed that the Soviets had many spy ships at sea and were engaged in obtaining our missile information and also information about the ocean approaches to the United States.

OTHER MILITARY TOPICS

In addition to these forces, there is an elite force of border troops, internal troops, and certain signal troops. The Soviet Government uses these security troops to maintain its hold on the country and also on the satellite nations.

It appears that the Soviet armed forces, in addition to their traditional large size, have finally achieved a balance, a maturity, and an excellence of performance. They have been reorganized and redeveloped in the postwar years under a long-range program of orderly development. This long-range program has been evidenced in officer training, continuous development of military production facilities, production of material, and the very high priority allocated to the development of artillery rockets and ballistic missiles. Despite shortcomings, the Soviet military machine today ranks among the best in the world both qualitatively and quantitatively.

Under Soviet regulations, all Soviet male citizens between the ages of nineteen through fifty who are physically eligible are subject to military service. There are approximately thirty-four and a half million men in this category. However, under peacetime only about 13½ per cent of this number are on active duty. During war, most of these would be mobilized. Conscription is regulated by the Military Service Law enacted in 1939 and later amended which calls for all citizens between nineteen and fifty to serve. Service in the reserves can constitute part of this requirement. Women in certain technical fields, in particular medical training, are also subject to military service.

Soviet males are usually called up for service when they reach nineteen. However, this is subject to the annual quota of the armed forces. Deferments are granted to various specialized workers and to students enrolled in schools of higher education. Almost one-half of each year's eligible class of about two million are required to meet the demands of the armed forces. Draftees are assigned to the various arms and services on the basis of their ability and training. Quotas for the various branches are fixed by the Council of Ministers and the Minister of Defense. Service time varies from three years in the ground, air, coast defense, and security forces, to four years for the naval forces. Although officer material is drawn from all classes, it works out that the Great Russians supply the largest contingent of officers because of:

higher education level

largest number of party members

On release from active service, each Soviet soldier is liable under the law for refresher training in the reserves. However, this law is believed to be weakly enforced because reservists are not normally spared from their civilian employment.

It is difficult to draw a true characterization of the individual Soviet soldier. Some Germans, for example, found him unpredictable while others depicted him as a formidable fighter, superbly trained, and highly disciplined. Others have called him uneducated, slovenly, and a peasant of semibarbaric nature. It is possible that all of these opinions may be partially valid. It is certain, however, that the official Communist portrayal of the ideal Soviet soldier is not a reliable guide and contains basic contradictions. Because of the heterogeneous nature of the Soviet populations, it is probably very difficult, if not impossible, to generalize on the character of the people. However, some generalizations can be made. Most are of peasant stock brought up under generations of hard manual labor. The peasant or collective farm worker of today may live in a sod or crude log cabin. The young city man usually lives with his family in a single shabby room. According to Communist standards, one person has the right to 9 square meters of living space. This is a little over 80 square feet! Thus, the young Soviet has known few comforts and very few luxuries. The Soviet soldier frequently finds army living standards and working conditions far superior to anything he has encountered in civilian life.

THE ROCKET COMPLEX

The rocket complex of the USSR is hard to illustrate because of its vastness and also because of its secret nature. Probably the main launch facilities for test operations are those at Kapustin Yar, although a new satellite launch facility has recently been opened at Aralsk; firings have been made from Franz Joseph Land, as previously mentioned; and it is reported that radar fixes from Finland and Turkey indicate that Lunik launchings have taken place from Irkutsk.

Despite all these evident scattered operations, however, according to the United States Navy's Pacific Missile Range, the Navy believes that the chief launch sites for development rockets is the one at Kapustin Yar near Stalingrad, on the shores of the Caspian Sea. This is the Soviet "Cape Canaveral". The new site at Aralsk, near the shores of the Aral Sea, is used for special shots (such as Sputniks and Luniks). The Navy also speculated on a possible new test site on the Peninsula of Kamchatka. The Caspian site, says the Navy, gives a range of

7,700 miles for the recent Soviet booster impacts in the Pacific Ocean near the Johnson Islands. The Aral site would give a range of about 6,150 miles.

However, the Russians claimed that the two firings of July 5 and July 7, 1960 had ranges of 13,000 kilometers (8,078 miles). Tass claimed these firings as new types of powerful multi-staged carrier rockets for space exploration. The impacts were observed by United States Navy patrol planes so these ranges have apparently been authenticated. The two tests made around the first of the year 1960, say the Soviets, were conducted from ranges of 7,760 miles.

What is it like at the Soviet Cape Canaverals? Each is in a semiarid region on a flat expanse that is ideal for situating launch pads. Large rail-mounted gantry (or service) towers slide back and forth for the big missiles. Scientists and workers probably live in drab barracks. The climate is cold in the winter and hot in the summer. Despite the fact that both of these bases are located near seas, they are probably more like our desert White Sands Proving Ground in New Mexico than our Florida base which is semitropical. The Soviets have one advantage. Their launch site is fairly well inland and test shots can be conducted and monitored via an all-ground system. Only recently, with the advent of the big new boosters, has there been need for ship tracking and observation.

Missile plants are located at: Irkutsk, Kalinin, Kazan, Kharkov, Kiev, Ryninski, Riga, Omsk, Novosibirsk, Leningrad, Moscow, Komsomolsk, Kuibyshev, Satatov, Sverdkovsky, Tashkent, and Ufa.

Rocket training schools are located at: Kaluga, Irkutsk, Novosibirsk, Sverdkovsky, Tashkent, and Ufa.

Rocket engine centers for development purposes are said to be located at: Ilmen, Irkutsk, Kalinin, Kazan, Riga, Omsk, Kapustin Yar, Kuibyshev, Kiev, Tomsk, and Peenemünde.

In addition other missile/space centers are 5 ground support electronics complexes, 14 truck-trailer plants, and 3 tracked-vehicle transport centers.

Thus, some 30 IRBM and 10 ICBM bases are in existence. Backing this up are 7 rocket schools, 17 rocket plants, and 11 rocket engine development centers. A Ford Foundation report recently stated that the USSR rocket force is estimated at 200,000 men! If this is true, then behind the lines there could be a backup force of about 300,000 administrators, scientists, engineers, technicians, and production workers. This makes a total rocket force of near half a million people, a tremendous pool of power. And when the USSR claims that it is unilaterally reducing its armed forces, it may mean that these are being shifted to a rocket force. At any rate, it is not believed that the Soviets are cutting their rocket forces; as a matter of fact, they are probably increasing them.

It seems to be the ultimate goal of the USSR to have 500 IRBM and ICBM's ready shortly for a TOT (time on target) attack. Coupled with a standing army of 175 modern and completely mechanized and mobile divisions, a fleet of turboprop and turbojet transports capable of rapid military conversion, and a huge naval fleet (said now to number more new and capital ships than the United States Navy) with a huge undersea striking force, it appears that the Red Giant could spring into action shortly after the button is pushed.

Most IRBM bases appear to be "soft," that is, vulnerable to attack. However, they are usually hidden in a small valley to minimize atomic blast (it would take an improbable direct hit to destroy them) and well protected by mobile AA rocket batteries. Most of such bases are actually located within the confines of the Soviet Union. On the other hand, most ICBM sites are probably "hard."

There are four IRBM complexes aimed at Britain and the Scandanavian countries: Kola, Ostrov, Ozera, and Ust-Taimyra. Eleven have assigned targets in Europe, northern Africa, and the Middle East: Bobruisk, Kazan, Kuressaare, Lada, Luga, Minsk, Odessa, Roslovl/Kirov, Riga, Seroc, Yelgava. Nine complexes are oriented toward Alaska, Japan, Okinawa, and other Asian targets: Anadyr, Irkutsk, Komsomolsk, Korsakov, Mil'kovo, Nikolaevsk, Okha, Omsk, and Terpeniye. This gives a total of over twenty operational IRBM bases—or about ten times the number of United States Thor/Jupiter bases! Further, it is believed that each Red IRBM base has at least ten missiles. Each Soviet IRBM would be able to carry a warhead approximating 25 megatons to a range of about 1,875 miles. This would amount to a target strike capability of about 6,770 megatons, equal to over 6 gigatons (billions of tons) of TNT vested within IRBM'S alone! It is probable that these bases are fully mobile and can be moved periodically to elude Western intelligence. Such bases would be difficult to pick up via the U-2 type of flight and almost impossible to pick up via an unmanned reconnaissance satellite.

Since the Soviet ICBM T-3 is of gigantic proportions (viz., booster thrust of 300,000 to 700,000 lbs.; launch weight on the order of 180,000 to 190,000 lbs.; base diameter of 15-20 ft.; and a total length of around 125 ft.), it is probable that great fixed bases (probably hardened to withstand atomic attack) exist. It is stated that the ICBM bases are all underground and able to stand overpressures of 150 lbs. per square inch. As a guide to blast damage, the United States Atomic Energy Commission states that only 2-3 psi. overpressure is enough to shatter non-reinforced concrete walls (12 in. thick); that an earth-covered reinforced concrete shelter collapses at 30-35 psi. overpressure; that aircraft (remember that a large liquid missile is quite flimsy in comparison to an aircraft) are completely destroyed by only 6 psi. overpressure. Peak overpressures of 90 psi. are experienced in an air burst with a 1 kiloton nuclear weapon bursting about 0.05 miles from target (ground zero) while for a surface burst, 100 psi. peak overpressures are experienced

about 0.07 miles away for the same kiloton bomb. The further
you are from ground zero point, the lower will be the pressure.
However, 1 kiloton yield weapons are now in the area of small
portable field weapons. For example, a peak overpressure of
2 psi. is experienced 5.3 miles away from ground zero in a
surface burst of 1 megaton (equal to 1 million tons of TNT).
And ICBM's and IRBM's will probably be carrying bigger yield
weapons than 1 megaton. Also, present ICBM accuracy is probably around 1 mile or so for ranges on the order of 5,000 to
6,000 miles.

The USSR is said to have a total of about 10 ICBM bases
actually operational. These "hard" underground sites are at
Alma-Ata, Anadyr, Aralsk, Irkutsk, Kapustin Yar, Komsomolsk,
Magnitogorsk, Mid Kalinin, Murgab, and Okha. A total of 10-
20 ICBM's (mostly aimed at America) are probably available
at each launch site. Thus, the Soviets have probably about 100
and perhaps 200 ICBM's in a ready-to-go state. Again this is
around 10:1 compared to those available here in America. With
Khrushchev's claim of ICBM production at 250 per year, it
looks as though the USSR will have an ultimate stockpile of
500-1,000 missiles ready to go. If we assume a "modest" 10
megaton warhead, this would mean about 5-10 gigatons men-
acing the United States. If the warheads are of the 25 megaton
variety, then it would be 12½ to 25 gigatons.

Coupled with other smaller but more numerous field weapons, the USSR could probably muster up, in the event of war,
a total of about 1 teraton of nuclear yield. One teraton would
equal 1 trillion tons of TNT.

Ground support equipment for liquid rockets usually is based
on tracked personnel carriers plus modified trucks and trailers.
The T-1 short-range ballistic rocket, for example, is an entirely
mobile weapon system. Another ground advantage of Soviet
missiles is their relatively large thrust-to-launch-weight ratio
(all over 2 and some 3 or 4 to one).

Most solid rockets are designed with mobility in mind. A great many are transported on tank chassis. Others are truck-hauled. With the exceptions of sub-launched missiles, all solid rockets are intended for use in battery-type fire and from non-permanent bases.

CHAPTER 4

THE HARDWARE

DEVELOPMENT and production of "hardware"—the physical realization of a technical concept—started hard on the heels of the end of World War II. We have seen that the Soviets were early to realize the importance of the rocket in furthering their Communist aims. Development—often using German weapons or designs as the starting point—was simple and straightforward. Thus, the Soviets did little to advance new and dramatic technology but preferred to stick to the tried and true and merely extend the state of the art, or to start by a slight extrapolation from what had already been known or done.

How was one to measure this hardware capability, particularly when details were likely to be hidden? Assuming that the Soviets would use the traditional or conventional approach, which they actually did, we might get a "look" at their hardware (or at least our concept of what their hardware might be like) by merely taking a possible or particular mission need and then designing a "look." This method is called "preliminary design" in rocket circles and the Soviets would have to go through the same steps.

In addition, these looks or preliminary designs can be organized into a logical, unified system of hardware. This is the procedure the author has followed. For the sake of clarity an arbitrary set of code numbers has been assigned to each possible missile or concept. The numbers, for example, are indicative of the advance of the state of development. This classification system is now widely used by most Western sources.

It then remained to collect all information coming out about each system until something more or less tangible or "coherent" was available. Many of these looks have now been crystallized by either direct views or by stated or measured performances. A famous crystallization was the massive "show-off" Red Square Parade of November 7, 1957. Little has appeared since then that has given Western eyes such a hard look at the Soviet missile effort. Whether newer views will again be presented is not known.

Liquid Rockets

The key to Soviet big-rocket progress can be traced to one thing: the early start on high thrust liquid rocket engines. Table 3 gives a brief technical summary of some of these engine developments.

The first Soviet task was the improvement of the German V-2 engine. At the end of the war, the Germans themselves had visualized many V-2 improvements and there was actual design and development work on higher thrust liquid rocket engines. The Soviets picked up these loose propulsion strings.

The original 56,000 lb. thrust V-2 engines were upgraded to about 77,000 to 78,000 lb. thrust. This was accomplished either by switching from the conventional water-alcohol fuel to the hotter burning kerosene and/or raising the combustion chamber pressure. Indeed, it is quite likely that both techniques were utilized. Minimum chamber pressures of 40-50 atmospheres were used. Then, new design and new materials also came along. For example, the Soviets were early to realize the benefits of using refractory coatings on metals. Metal oxide coatings on such "exotic" metals as tantalum, columbium, or tungsten

TABLE 3   LIQUID ENGINES

| | Engine Designation | | | |
Engine Parameter	Soviet V-2 (T-1)	R-10	R-14	R-14A
Sea level thrust, lbs.	55,000	77,000	220,000	264,000
Vacuum thrust, lbs.	66,500	90,500	262,000	298,000
Thrust, metric tons	26	35	100	120
Engine diameter, in.	36.3	36.3	—	—
Nozzle length, in.	34.4	45.5	115.5	88
Throat diameter, in.	15.75	15.75	14.92	15.8
Exit diameter, in.	29.1	33.4	59.8	50
Oxidizer	LOX	LOX	LOX	LOX
Fuel	Water-Alcohol	Water-Alcohol	Kerosene	Kerosene
Oxidizer/Fuel Ratio	1.23	1.23	2.28	2.28
Specific Impulse, sea level, sec.	210	211	242	250
Specific Impulse, vacuum, sec.	253	248	288	282
Flow rate, lb./sec.	262	365	910	1056
L^{*1}	113	113	—	—
Combustion pressure, psi.	220	289	850	882

[1] L^{*} = Characteristic chamber length. See Glossary.

may have been used, although it is more likely that upgraded steels were used. Also, at the same time, better cooling methods were devised. Eventually the Russians were probably able to up-rate the V-2 type of engine to a new high thrust of about 99,000 lbs. Reports have stated that, although the engine is designed for operation on LOX (liquid oxygen) and a hydrocarbon fuel, other propellant combinations could be used. The storable combinations such as nitric acid or nitrogen tetroxide would fall into this category. Most of this preliminary work had been accomplished by about 1948-1950.

The next logical step must then have been the development of a large, single-chamber thrust unit of about 220,000 lbs. (100,000 kg.) thrust. The German Sänger had been working on just such a development as the 100 metric ton thrust engine at the end of the war. His approach was the use of a very high combustion chamber pressure, a brazed tubing nozzle and combustion chamber, and LOX and a hydrocarbon fuel (spiked with a high energy component such as aluminum metal powder). Therefore, the Soviets might well have taken over from this very point. Germans who worked for the Soviets on missile programs state that the 100 metric ton thrust unit was the one postulated for them by the Soviets for their IRBM work in all their studies. Again, there was no "exotic" work involved, simply the extension of what already looked feasible.

The big step that probably was taken was the use of still higher combustion chamber pressures (vis., near 900 psi.). The availability of this engine meant that the IRBM could become an operational reality by 1955. It is interesting to note that about this time, and especially at the time of the Suez Canal crisis, the Soviets began using the now current tactic of "ballistic blackmail," or "rocket rattling." It is quite likely that further scale-up has taken place since 1955 and that, for example, the R-14A engine is capable of producing 264,000 lb. thrust at sea level and 298,000 lb. thrust under space conditions. One of these engines could easily power an IRBM and two such engines would power a long-range, heavy payload ICBM. Figure 2, p. 77, shows engine lineup.

By comparison the USAF Atlas uses two 165,000 lb. thrust engines for its booster (for a total of 330,000 lb. boost thrust); the USAF Titan uses two 150,000 lb. thrust engines (for a total of a 300,000 lb. boost thrust) in its first or booster stage.

There is now good evidence that a single chamber engine of 400,000 to 600,000 lb. thrust is in existence, at least for some special Soviet shots.

It should be emphasized that all run-of-the-mill Soviet missiles used for military purposes in the long-range category are operated on standard LOX-hydrocarbon fuels. It could be, though, that for special purposes (viz., space shots), "spiked" fuels could be used for slight additional energy gains. A spiked fuel is a standard fuel used with additional higher energy fuels to give a higher performing propellant. The Soviets have mentioned special fuels (borons, amines, or hydrazines) in their literature. It is quite likely that these special fuels may have been used to yield more than just marginal performance on their special missions such as the Sputniks or Luniks. However, because of the size, performance, and payload capabilities of their military IRBM's and ICBM's, it is unlikely that "exotic" propulsion methods are being used.

Another possibility is that the Soviets could add high energy materials to the oxidizer. Both fluorine and ozone are known to perform better than the standard liquid oxygen. Liquid fluorine is just now coming into its own here in the United States and our ozone work has apparently fallen by the wayside. On the other hand, the Soviets have been especially active in ozone research. So, ozone additions to liquid oxygen remain a possibility.

And yet another word about Soviet rocket engine work. From need, to design, to construction, to testing, to production mating with the actual missile is very short—about two years at the most. This is from one-half to one-tenth the time a comparable development takes in the United States.

It is now possible to summarize Soviet liquid rocket engine work. By and large, unusual or pioneering approaches have not been taken. LOX is the standard oxidizer, while hydrocarbon fuels are used. Performance is obtained through high combustion chamber pressures. Engines have been scaled up to meet the more than marginal demands of a reliable military missile system. This reliability has paid off in the special space

TABLE 4 LIQUID ROCKETS

Designation	Thrust (lbs.)	Launch Weight (lbs.)	Length (ft.)	Diameter (ft.)	Range (mi.)	Remarks
T-1	78,000	38,000	50-52	5.15	250	Single-stage—improved V-2.
T-1A	99,000	44,000	50-52	5.15	350	Single-stage—improved T-1.
T-2	78,000 #2 268,000 #1	110,000	90-100	12-15	1,875	Two stages. Upper stages use modified T-1 or T-1A.
T-3	78,000 #3 268,000 #2 440,000 #1	180,000	100-125	16	5,500	Three stages. Probably modified for Sputnik & Lunik.
T-3A	520,000 #1	185,000	112	16	6,200	Three stages.
T-3B	720,000 #1				8,700	Three stages.
T-4	600,000 #1	232,000	120-125	10-12	12,000	Manned orbital rocket.
Golem 1	120,000	75,000	54	5.41	400	Single stage. Sub-towed rocket device. Nitric acid/kerosene.
Golem 2	242,000	75,000	57	7.2		Two stages. Sub rocket. Nitric acid and kerosene propellant.

shots also. However, this is not meant to imply that the Soviets have not had their share of failures. They do have an advantage in that they can keep news of failures from leaking out. And, by the way, they can even keep successful firings under their hat if they so desire.

Because developments are rapid in the USSR, we should expect that newer techniques will be employed in future engines. There is considerable talk now about the use of storable systems. A storable liquid rocket would make for rapid activation when and if any panic button is pushed. Fuel additives are a distinct possibility. New oxidizers (such as fluorine and other "novel" compounds) are also possible. Hydrogen apparently is also being given considerable attention, especially for space work.

The big striking force of the USSR today is vested within its long-range missile arsenal. As previously stated, except for special aircraft rockets for the Air Force, and the submarine rockets of the Navy, all rockets are unified into a single command under the jurisdiction of the Army.

Table 4 gives known or calculated specifications for the liquid rockets of the USSR. The most important are the big four ballistic missiles. Figure 3 sketches a preliminary design layout for the operational ones, the T-1 (short-range), the T-2 (IRBM), and the T-3 (ICBM). Plate 7 shows a photograph of the T-1, the only large liquid rocket seen with sufficient clarity by Western eyes and the camera.

T-1

This T-1, the "Sovietized" V-2 was first seen by Westerners in 1957. It is not only similar in design and operation to the V-2, its ancestor, but also to the American Redstone missile (which is also related to the V-2). Photos have shown that the missile is light enough to be towed by a truck–trailer combination. However, it has also been pulled by a half-track type of truck. It is fueled on the launch pad and fired vertically. Preliminary trajectory control is given by short aerodynamic fins and by carbon vanes in the exhaust stream. The conical nose indicates a range of around 250 miles. Longer ranges would imply greater velocities and these greater velocities

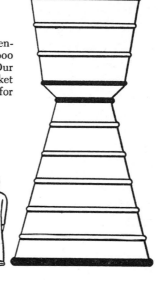

Lineup of current Soviet liquid rocket engines (l. to r.) 220,000 lb. thrust; 550,000 lb. thrust; and 1,100,000 lb. thrust. Our nearest comparable unit is the Saturn rocket (1,500,000 lb. thrust). Not yet ready for full flight test.

Figure 2

would mean severe aerodynamic heating for the warhead with a streamlined nose cone.

In missiles with a range of over 500 miles the recent trend has been to use the blunt type of nose cone which, in conjunction with heat sink or ablation cooling, insures that the payload will survive the severe re-entry conditions. Some plumbing and/or wiring runs externally from the forward control section to the aft engine section. Fill ports are discernible. In addition, vent ports indicate the use of a non-storable propellant such as LOX. Because this missile has been publicly shown, it is quite possible that it has now been relegated to the obsolescence heap. More likely, however, it is being used for training purposes and may well wind up in the hands of the satellite nations and Red China. It is quite likely that Red China, or any of the other satellites, could utilize the T-1 to place a 25-50 lb. satellite into orbit in the near future.

Although the T-1 missile may be near obsolescence, it is a potent weapon. It could probably carry a very large kiloton warhead or possibly a small megaton bomb. All indications are that the Soviets would plan to use the T-1 in any giant mobile sweep across Europe. It would be used for large targets of opportunity and for reaching those previously out-of-range targets (or those missed by IRBM or ICBM attacks) which come into range as the front advances.

Another use of the T-1 is expected to come from the satellite nations or Red China may establish its own satellite and thus give prestige to a regime the Soviets are trying to persuade the rest of the world to accept. Table 5 shows the capabilities of the T-1 for giving Sputniki for Sputniki (satellites for the satellites).

TABLE 5   SPUTNIKI FOR SPUTNIKI

Satellite Weight (lbs.)	Launching Vehicle Weight, Total, (lbs.)	Booster Stage Thrust (lbs.)	Remarks
25	50,000	78,000	Standard T-1 and engine plus small upper-stage solid rockets or clusters of solid rockets.
50	75,000	80,000	Upgraded T-1 and engine and/or upper stage(s).
50	50,000	80,000	Upgraded T-1 and engine and better mass ratio in booster rocket.

A most likely candidate for the "satellite club" would be Red China. The Chinese Communists are reported to have been working on their own satellite (with Soviet aid) now for a number of years. Launching should soon be expected. If the matter of East Germany (the East German Democratic Republic) is not resolved soon, then the Soviets can also be expected to conclude a separate treaty with this nation and give it world prestige by helping it to launch its own satellite.

The T-1 could be rigged to launch a small (around 25 lb.) satellite without too much modification. The approach, similar to that already taken by the United States Army with its Redstone (the Jupiter-C which launched this country's first satellite, the "Explorer"), that is by upgrading thrust and adding two stages of small, existing military solid propellant artillery rockets, would suffice to put a satellite into orbit with a minimum amount of time.

Yet another interesting international implication of the T-1 would catch the United States with its "policy down." The T-1, in the hands of the Red Chinese, could easily bombard Formosa from launch sites deep within the mainland. If conventional explosives were used, what would our policy be? Remember that the Reds consider rockets as artillery and artillery is now used to plaster the offshore islands at least every other day!

T-2

There are two different views of this IRBM. The early view was that this missile was two-staged. For example, a T-1, or modification thereof, was simply placed atop a larger booster rocket. The other view, as given by German returnees, is that the missile may have had only one stage. Either way you look at it, the main power plant is in the 100 metric ton (about 220,000 lb.) thrust class.

A more conservative approach (and for this reason this may be the more likely) would be to use two stages. The 100 metric ton thrust booster could be tested separately.

Thus, as indicated in Table 4, the T-2 would have a launch weight of about 110,000 lbs. and a total length of 90-100 ft. Booster diameter would be on the order of 12-15 ft.

A more radical approach would be to design this IRBM as a single-stage vehicle. USSR Project R-14 (or G-4) studied the single-stage concept from the end of World War II to around 1950. The Germans in Russia, for example, worked on this paper project. Their designs were for an IRBM of 1,875 mile range, and using a single chamber, single engine of 220,000 lb. thrust. Payload was to have been a 6,620 lb. package. Loaded weight was 160,000 lbs. and burnout weight (with payload) was to have been 15,400 lbs. Emphasis was placed on existing propulsion methods (LOX-hydrocarbons) using a combustion chamber pressure of 900 psi. This approach indicated that by good design practices a small fraction of the rocket must be dead weight. For example, the studies showed the possibility of a burnout weight of only 10 per cent of the launch weight, viz., 90 per cent propellants. According to known rocket principles you can better the performance of any rocket by increasing the exhaust velocity of the rocket and/or loading as much propellant as possible into a given vehicle. Thus, although this approach of bettering the mass ratio, as it is called, could have been taken, it would require considerably more effort (and hence time) than the conventional multi-staged approach. It is an axiom in rocket work that by the use of multiple stages, you throw away, so to speak, your design inefficiencies. In a single-stage vehicle, you have to live with them all the time. Therefore, multiple staging is a quick way out of the performance puzzle, but you pay for it in a relatively heavy total mass.

It is believed that the Red IRBM's started to roll off the assembly lines somewhere around 1955, and by 1957 were presumed to be available in sufficient numbers for the start of the Soviet "ballistic blackmail" policy program. According to

Western intelligence sources, something like 200 IRBM's had been test-fired before the period 1958-1959. As a comparison, only about one-third to one-half of this number had been fired by the United States in Thor and Jupiter tests. As a matter of fact, the Soviets have done much better. They have fired their IRBM in tests involving troops maneuvering in both the firing and target zones; in addition, the Soviets managed to fire these IRBM's with live warheads before the present nuclear test ban went into voluntary effect. To date, the United States (at least officially) has not had any experience in firing its IRBM's (or ICBM's for that matter) with live nuclear warheads.

Whether the Red IRBM is one- or two-staged is not important. From 500 to 1,000 of these missiles are probably in existence at the present time. They have sufficient range to cover most of Europe, England, and North Africa from within the confines of the USSR itself. However, it will not be surprising to see them set up in Africa, Red China, and Cuba as well. Indeed Cuba has already stated that Soviet missile aid has been accepted.

There are at present some 30 known IRBM sites. Most of these are within the USSR. All are on a rail route from the factory to the emplacement sites. Most of these IRBM sites are mobile and quite probably of the "soft" (that is relatively vulnerable to atomic attack) or the semi-hard variety (viz., launch pads and storage sites protected by blast walls). These IRBM bases are probably tied into the regular defense communications network and are protected by radar and antiaircraft guided missile systems.

It is significant to note that most of the Soviet IRBM's are Europe-oriented. About three-quarters of the IRBM's are probably intended for European targets.

The existence of the T-2 in, say, Cuba would pose an extremely serious threat to the United States. One point is the matter of warning. All our ballistic missile warning nets are oriented along the Arctic toward the USSR. Thus, Soviet missiles could enter the United States along our "soft and unprotected under flanks." Second, an IRBM could be more accurate than a longer range ICBM. Also, for shorter ranges, larger warheads could be carried. Now with the over 5,000 lb. warhead capability of the T-2 (it is probably near 7,000 lbs. now and could probably carry a 10,000 lb. warhead for shorter ranges), this would immediately raise the possibility of 25-50 megatons of H-weapons! And, practically all of important American targets are well within the range of a 1,875 mile missile firing from Cuba.

It is believed that the T-2 (or possibly the T-3 below) may have formed the basis for the Sputnik and Lunik launching vehicles. These are described in greater detail in Chapter 5 (Sputniks) and Chapter 6 (Luniks and Beyond).

T-3

This ICBM is probably the world's biggest and most operational of rockets. Ranges of 5,500 to 8,700 miles are possible. The latest (two pairs each) of firings into the Pacific Ocean indicate the capabilities of a powerful booster rocket which probably was modified from the first or booster stage of the T-3 ICBM.

The Soviet ICBM would have to have at least two stages and more probably it has three stages. A logical development would take a T-2 type of vehicle (with some possible scaling down or weight shaving) and build a big booster rocket for the first stage. This would call for a booster thrust of 300,000 to 700,000 lbs. One gets thrust requirements of this order of magnitude when one works back from payloads orbited with the Sputniks and Luniks and ranges attained in the recent Pacific plunkings. Thus, the Soviet ICBM is probably much larger than either of the United States ICBM's (Atlas and Titan). This is probably because the missile design was completed before the advent of small, high-yield hydrogen warheads. The latter has paid off for the Soviets. They did not wait for small weapons. They did not wait for the emergence of exotic materials or propellants. They did not wait for miniaturized electronic guidance systems. They started with the development of large rockets to begin with. However, when the smaller nuclear weapons did become available, the development of large rockets first paid off in better performance, longer ranges, or the use of higher yield weapons.

Some 10 ICBM bases (said to be hard) are supposed to exist. More are probably slated. Khrushchev has stated that Soviet ICBM production is 250 per year. It is thus likely that the Soviets now have about 100 ICBM's ready to go. The United States, on the other hand, has about a tenth of that number.

T-4

The T-4 is looked on as a Soviet extension of the Sänger antipodal bomber. The original concept was to have used a large booster rocket which pushed a winged rocket along kilometers-long rails to get up speed. Then, when supersonic, the pilot would kick in his rocket engine of 100 metric tons thrust (please note!) and be boosted to the very fringes of the earth's atmosphere—several hundred miles' altitude. The winged rocket would not be in orbit, however, but would be drawn back to earth by gravity. However, the pilot could extend his stay in space by executing a series of entries and exits to and from the atmosphere—much like a stone skipping along the top of the water when thrown properly—hence, called the "skip" bomber. This would allow this manned rocket missile to reach any spot on the earth. During the forties, however, this concept didn't get very far because it could only carry a payload of around 1 metric ton (2,200 pounds). The pilot in his mission either would have to perish with his intended target or eject himself before reaching the target.

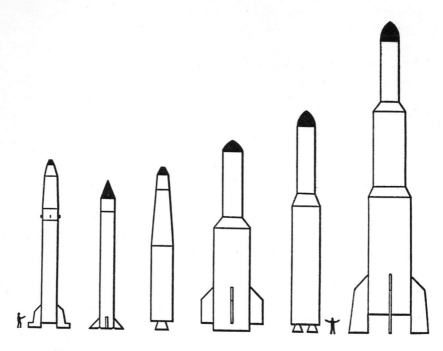

Figure 3

U. S. vs. USSR liquid ballistic rockets. (L. to r.): medium range
U. S. Redstone and T-1; IRBM Thor and T-2; ICBM Titan and
T-3. With exception of medium range missiles, all USSR missiles
are bigger and heavier than comparable U. S. version.

The Soviet's keen interest in such a development was clearly indicated when Stalin sent his son Vasily to Paris in his unsuccessful attempt to lure Sänger back to Russia.

However, reports have constantly been seeping out of Russia about the continuance of the antipodal bomber concept. Recently, this concept has been started in development in the United States as the Dyna-Soar project. It may be that the Soviet man-in-space program will take this approach. The recent Sputnik IV shot certainly indicated that the manned satellite is probably the next space step. This possibility will be covered in greater detail in Chapter 5 (Sputniks) in the section on the manned space station.

Anti-ICBM

It appears that the Soviets, at least since 1957, have been keenly interested in the development of an anti-ICBM missile system—the so-called anti-missile missile. According to V. Kriksunov, an engineer-major, radar can detect the ICBM at ranges of 320 miles and predict its course and impact point via computers. This computation must be done in about a minute. To be sure that the ICBM is destroyed 50 miles from its intended target, the anti-missile must be fired when the incoming ICBM is still 169 miles away. This leaves something like 25-30 seconds for a computer solution of an intercept course. Therefore, detection at ranges of 810-1,000 miles is to be preferred. The detection accuracy of 1957 systems was stated to be 1 per cent—or within 10 miles—for a radar with a 1,000 mile radar detection range. A 20 kiloton warhead is assumed for the anti-ICBM missile and, therefore, the Soviet goes on, the anti-missile missile must intercept the incoming ICBM with an accuracy of better than 985 feet. A configuration is presented which gives a third stage weight of 945 lbs., powered flight time of 30 sec., initial launch weight of 95,500 lbs., and a booster thrust of 308,000 lbs. for a three-stage anti-ICBM. However, the Soviets believe that better aiming accuracies can be achieved. The Soviets do not believe, states Kriksunov, that the ICBM is the ultimate weapon. An anti-ICBM system is fully technically feasible. In the meantime, the United States anti-ICBM program has been dragging despite the efforts of the United States Army to display experimentally the feasibility of their Nike-Zeus system.

Computers, vital in any possible anti-ICBM program, have been the subject of Soviet complaints. The Kremlin has allocated two billion rubles per year to be spent on "electronic information-processing digital computers" until 1965. Academician Axel I. Berg, however, complains in *Izvestia* (June 12, 1960) that the low quality of radio electronics instrumentation is slowing progress on electronic computers and guidance systems. In *Komsomolskaya Pravda* (June 11, 1960), A. Musatkin said that new Soviet computers were still using old tubes in place of the more modern transistors. Computer personnel shortages are also claimed. The Bauman Technical School (Moscow) has graduated only 40 computer engineers so far. An additional 200 graduate students are in training at the University of Moscow for eventual computer work at Novosibirsk in 1961.

What is some of the Soviet electronics gear like? Based on electronic devices seen in the Soviet Union and equipment displayed here in the United States, the general concensus seems to be that there is little to choose from in the way of standard equipment. There is no streamlining, no miniaturization, and the equipment usually has a bulky but functional appearance. Units displayed here in the United States were rated by United States electronic manufacturers as being five to ten years behind us. Again the comment was that the equipment was useful but appeared ugly. According to the Soviets, a pleasing design just for the sake of appearance is a sign of the decadent. Reliability is achieved through brute force. They overdesign.

Where we would use a half-watt resistor, the Soviets would use a two-watt rating. And the Soviets have no qualms about incorporating the designs or workings of others into their own systems.

Other Liquid Rockets

We have seen how fuzzy our view of liquid rockets has become as we have progressed along the line of bigger and bigger missiles. The Soviets constantly say that the details or hardware of their technology are not important (meaning that they don't want us to know about them) and that only their mere existence or actual performances are important.

There are two other large liquid rockets that should be mentioned. Both of these are believed to be useful in the development of the storable rocket and the submarine rockets.

Very early in the fifties, the Soviets started to expand their submarine force. At first, it was believed that they used the cruise type of missile which could be launched from surfaced subs only. Then, sub-towed rockets using nitric acid oxidizer systems (storable) were reported (Golem 1 and Golem 1A). However, it is now believed that because of solid propellant developments, these storable combinations might soon be applied to missiles like the T-1 and bigger. The work on solids, discussed below, is believed to be as advanced as our Polaris system which can launch IRBM's from a submerged submarine.

Solid Rockets

As pointed out earlier, the Soviets have a heavy background in solid propellant artillery rockets stemming from World War II. Because of the pressing needs of the battlefield, most if not all of their solid propellant technology was pressed into production of millions of small artillery rockets. However, the Rus-

sians were very quick to adapt such German solid rockets as
antitank and aircraft rockets to their use.

Not only was there a lag in the use and general application
of solid rockets to their needs, but there was a general lack of
technology in the area of solid propellants. It was not until after
World War II that modern solid propellant technology got
started. For example, the gun propellants limited rocket applications to the very small grains needed for short-range artillery
rockets. Only after the war, with the advent of composite
propellants, was the large solid rocket feasible.

Table 6 lists important solid rockets. All of these have been
seen and photographed with the exception of the submarine-

TABLE 6   SOLID ROCKETS

Name	Mis-sion	Length (ft.)	Diam-eter (ft.)	Remarks
T-5	S-S[1]	37.4	ca.1.0	4 stages. Gun-launched. Atomic warhead. Development of German *Rheinbote*.
T-5B	S-S	25-30	ca.2.5	Single stage? Six canted nozzles. Double-base propellant. Similar to Honest John. Atomic warhead; 10-15 mile range.
T-5C	S-S	25-35	ca.2.0	Single stage? Smaller version of T-5B. Atomic warhead; 5-10 mile range.
T-6	S-A[2]	22	2.79	Two stages plus cluster of four boosters. About 25 miles slant range. Ceiling is approximately 50-70 thousand ft.
T-7A	S-S	25	3.0	Single stage. 17,000 lb. thrust for 30-60 seconds. Composite propel-lant. Weight is around 7½ tons. About 50 miles range. Atomic war-head. Similar to U.S. Sergeant. T-7A, however, is tank-transported.

(TABLE 6—Contd.)

Name	Mission	Length (ft.)	Diameter (ft.)	Remarks
T-7B	S-S	30	4.0	Single stage; 100 mile range improvement of T-7A. In U.S. Pershing missile class.
M-2	S-A	24.9	1.6	Two stages; 25-50 miles slant range. Ceiling of 50-70 thousand ft. 3,950 lb. launch weight.
M-100A	A-A[3]	4.33	0.26	IR or radar guided; 3-5 miles range. Maximum speed is about 1,750 mph. In class with U.S. Super Falcon.
CH-17B (Komet 1)	US-S[4]	42		Underwater launched. Single stage; 10 mile range. 53,250 lb. thrust. Development rocket only.
CH-18B	US-S	42.3	5.9	Underwater launched from submarine. Single stage. 99,000 lb. thrust. 41,350 lb. launch weight. 620 mile range. Operational.
CH-19 (Komet 3)	US-S			Underwater launched from submarine. Two stages; 1,200-1,875 mile range. Near operational.

[1] S-S: surface-to-surface (artillery)
[2] S-A: surface-to-air (antiaircraft)
[3] A-A: air-to-air (aircraft rocket)
[4] US-S: undersea-to-surface (sub-launch)

launched rockets. A brief review of these important solid rockets follows.

T-5

This four-stage rocket, though not seen, was deduced from the huge barrel-type launcher mounted atop a heavy duty tank chassis. The large diameter of the barrel, the light construction, and the relatively light recoil mechanism has led experts to believe that this weapon is in reality a gun-launched rocket. The Germans had fired their *Rheinbote* a distance of over 120 miles during World War II and were thinking about the use of a launching barrel. For more details, consult the section on hybrid rockets later in this chapter.

T-5B

First seen in the Moscow parade of 1957, this surface-to-surface missile resembles our Honest John. However, it is mounted and fired like a cannon from its tank chassis carrier. In this respect it is more mobile than the United States Honest John which has to be positioned via a crane and is carried by a truck. The six canted nozzles on the T-5B indicate spin stabilization and also the possible use of a double base propellant. The large and bulbous nose is probably nuclear. One interesting feature is the encasing cylindrical tube which is highly ribbed. Though it could be a firing tube, there are lines which indicate that the tube could open up like a clamshell. Indeed, there are also visible hydraulically operated piston actuators which seem to be used for opening. Therefore this device could be a heater which keeps the missile propellant warm during firing. This, then, would lead one to believe that a double-base solid propellant might be used. Usually double-base propellants (containing nitrocellulose and nitroglycerin) are much more sensitive to low temperatures than composites. A low propellant temperature causes the propellant to burn at a lower rate than at normal room temperatures. This slower burning, in turn, causes the missile thrust to be lower than designs call for. Because the thrust is lower and the burning time is longer, the missile will fly over a different trajectory than that intended, say, at room temperatures. The remedy, therefore, is to warm the propellant—especially during very cold weather. The United States Honest John, for example, also uses a double-base propellant, and an electrically heated blanket must be used to keep the missile warm before firing. However, the blanket must be removed manually before firing. The Soviet system would seem to offer distinct battlefield advantages in that it could be more rapidly fired than the Honest John.

T-5C

This missile was also seen for the first time in 1957. It resembles the T-5B, but appears to be somewhat scaled down. It has a somewhat smaller diameter than its big brother. However, the warhead is about the same size and this indicates either improved performance or a smaller range. The T-5C is mounted on a highly mobile tank chassis which is equipped for amphibious operations. This chassis appears to be much lighter than the one for the T-5B, also indicating a lighter missile.

T-6

Also known as the M-1, this missile was an early antiaircraft and is similar in operational capability to the United States Nike-Ajax. Operational at an early date, it could have been the type the Russians claimed downed the American U-2 spy plane in May 1960.

The Soviet publication, *Izvestia*, cited Major Michael R. Voronov as commander of the rocket battery that shot down the U-2 plane. Marshal Sergei S. Biryuzov, who became head of all antiaircraft defenses in 1954, said the use of rockets will make possible a substantial cut in antiaircraft troops. One rocket, manned by only three men, can take the place of an entire conventional artillery battalion of six hundred men.

Radar is a well-developed monitoring item in the USSR. Soviet radar can spot a "metallic flea" in the stratosphere. It is divided into zones of several hundred kilometers of air space. These zones are tied into a net called a "unified radar field." Each field is further tied to the others.

T-7A

This is a large, modern solid rocket that is similar to our Sergeant missile. However, the Russian model is fired vertically after riding to the battlefield launch site on its tank chassis. It is patterned after the early German *Wasserfall* rocket, but has been adapted for surface-to-surface use. Total weight is about 7½ tons, and it carries an atomic warhead. Its crew is minimum —it probably can be set up and fired by two or three men. Its range is about 30-50 miles. The T-7A has been operational for a number of years—probably since around 1955. In 1957, models similar to the T-7A were seen in Poland and were claimed to have been used by a Polish aeronautical institute for high altitude rocket work. Within the year 1960 this same missile was displayed in the hands of the Red Chinese. Photograph Plate 9 illustrates this missile.

T-7B

An improved version of the T-7A, the T-7B model is undergoing range modifications. Reports state that a 100-mile range can be expected. This then indicates that the missile is starting to approach the United States Pershing class. It is believed that the newer missile will also ride to battle atop a tank chassis rather than resort to a truck carrier. Addition of an upper stage could make this a submarine or IRBM rocket of around 1,500 mile range.

M-2

First seen in 1957, this antiaircraft rocket is a modern, radar or IR (infrared) guided, two-stage design that is similar to our Nike-Hercules rocket. It probably can carry an atomic warhead. More important, it is designed to be a completely mobile system and can be easily transported to protect the front as it moves. Also, it probably can be used in a mobile system within the Soviet Union in order to keep defense security at a maximum. The United States has relied on known and fixed AA missile sites for both models of Nike and also for the Bomarc.

SUBMARINE MISSILES

Though not yet seen, reliable reports state that the Soviets have worked on submarine-launched missiles for a time at least equivalent to that of the United States Polaris program. The CH ("Komet") series of sub-launched rockets are said to have progressed from an initial range of 10 to 1,200 miles and beyond. All are solid missiles. The significance of such missiles cannot be minimized. With its three-sided seacoast border, most of the United States is highly vulnerable to a missile attack from subs. Moreover, such an attack could almost come as a complete surprise at the present state of our warfare art. Also, we have no adequate missile warning net which is oriented to monitor possible attacks from the Atlantic, Pacific, or the Gulf of Mexico. Prime targets line our coast. A one- or two hundred-mile belt along our coasts includes most of the major industrial capacity of the nation. Ballistic missile launch capabilities have definitely been identified with much of the several odd hundred "obsolete" conventionally powered ships in the Soviet submarine fleet.

Recently the United States has been plagued by Soviet "fishing" vessels, disturbing cables, monitoring missile firings, and generally ferreting out our antisubmarine defenses. Not only has the USSR invested heavily in "basic" oceanographic studies but she has recently commissioned a fleet of some 200 modern "trawlers" equipped with the latest radar, sonar, and other electronic snooping gear. It can be summarized that the USSR will utilize the submarine to the greatest possible extent.

It is also possible to generalize on Soviet solid rocket developments:

1. Double-base propellants still seem to be standard for short-

range artillery work. However, there is a growing trend toward composites for longer ranges. The USSR trails the United States in long-range solid missiles but excels in shorter range battlefield rockets. Standard specific impulses of homogeneous propellants are on the order of 200-225 seconds and there is a growing trend toward upgrading the double-base propellants by the addition of high-energy components such as aluminum, boron, etc. It has been stated that the Soviets have large propellant extrusion presses which enable production of grains about 1 meter (3.28 ft.) in diameter. Casting techniques are also being utilized. There is a concerted effort to evolve a double-base propellant with a specific impulse of 250-275 seconds. This may be done through compounding with composites.

2. The growth of composites has been much slower in the USSR than in the United States. The reason probably was the lack of adequate polymeric fuel-binders (viz., plastics). Several years ago large efforts were put into the expansion of Soviet and satellite nation plastics facilities. The epoxy plastics as well as the polyurethane were among the leaders in the expansion process. Both are potential high-energy and most useful fuel-binders for solid propellants. In addition, the epoxy plastics are most useful for the ablation type of nose cone and for glass fiber-plastic structural laminates now extensively used in the missile field. It is believed that from the start the Soviets used the ablation type of nose cone for all those missiles of longer range which face severe re-entry conditions in their hypersonic plunge to their targets. In addition, there is a report of much work in the Soviet Union devoted to studies of mixed inorganic oxidizers. This is probably due to a search for better low-temperature performing propellants. Recently the Soviets reported work on the use of a potent new inorganic oxidizer, hydroxylamine perchlorate. This decomposes without explosion (at 180° C.) into

ammonium perchlorate and oxygen. Ammonium perchlorate is the standard United States composite oxidizer. Present standard composite performance in the USSR is seen to be around 240 sec. (at 1,000 psi.) with increases being sought in the 250-275 sec. range.

3. Scale-up of solid units has taken place. The 1 million lb. sec. unit of the T-7A has been operational for at least five years. A new solid booster of 80,000 to 99,000 lb. thrust is available.

4. Standards of Soviet solid rockets are generally poorer than the United States in terms of elegance but are superior in terms of field usability. Only recently have there been any efforts to improve the mass ratio of their solid rockets.

5. Guidance is relatively crude. Early guidance was simply ballistic, with performance being determined by thrust and burn time (which are built into the grain). Apparently this is still the favored line of attack. Warhead guidance with infrared (IR) or radar has shown remarkable development and is now somewhat comparable to that of United States guidance.

Cruise Missiles, Ramjets, and Hybrid Rockets

In addition to making huge efforts toward the development of liquid and solid rockets, the Soviets were early to exploit the pulsejet, turbojet, ramjet, and hybrid rockets for new military uses.

It is certain that the Soviets started with the German V-1 cruise-type missile. Very early after the end of the war, the Soviets produced an almost exact copy of the V-1. This was the J-1 pulsejet. Some 500 are said to have been built. These were perhaps used for actual interim defense but more probably for training while the larger ballistic missiles were being developed. In addition, they were used for propulsion and guidance tests and quite likely wound up as target drones. The

Red Army is said to have employed the J-1 from emplaced po-
sitions; however, truck launchers soon became available. The
J-1 had a diameter of about 3 ft., a fuselage length of 30 ft.,
and a wing span of 23 ft. Its top speed was around 400 miles
per hour and its range well over 300 miles. The Red Navy also
early used this weapon to train crews of subs in the launching
of guided missiles. Then Soviet developments came along and
offered further weapons improvements.

Axial compressor turbojet engines, the RD-10 (a copy of the
German Jumo 004 turbojet), and the RD-20 (a copy of the
BMW 003) may have been used for early cruise missile development. During the period 1945-1947, these engines were
available in large numbers since they were used for jet fighter
propulsion. It is possible that the new engines were mated to
the J-2. The J-2 is looked on as having a diameter of 4½ ft., a
length of 36 ft., and a span of around 25 ft. The subsonic craft
had a range of about 500 miles and could carry a nuclear warhead. Its present competitors in the United States are the Air
Force Mace (formerly the Matador) and the Navy's Regulus.
The RD-45F (centrifugal flow) engine of 5,000 lb. thrust may
also have been used on Soviet cruise weapons starting around
1948. The RD-45F engine was used in the famous MIG-15. The
VK-1 engine (7,500 lb. thrust with afterburner) may also have
been used on later cruise missile models. Production models of
the MIG-17 used the VK-2 engine of 6,000 lb. thrust, while
the VK-5 engine of 8,690 lb. thrust was used to propel the
Yak-25. However, this was apparently the end of the road for
turbojet-powered cruise missiles. Around 1948, for example,
development began on the 15,000 to 19,000 lb. thrust turbojet
engines for long-range jet bombers.

The next logical propulsion step may have been to employ
the ramjet. The J-3 thus may have been the last of the chem-
ically powered cruise missiles. During J-3's time, increasing attention was being given to getting the long-range ballistic
missile into operation.

In early 1939 Polikarpov and Markrelov tested ramjets in the USSR. By the year of 1940, two ramjets were flight tested under the wings of the I-153 fighter airplane. In 1944 the Yak-7 flew with ramjets. At present work with supersonic ramjets is continuing and a nuclear ramjet is also reported.

Unlike the United States, the USSR took an active interest in developing hybrid rockets. Indeed these actually reached the production stage. First view of a small hybrid rocket came in 1956. When the British landed at Port Said, they captured numbers of Soviet-made rocket rifles for antitank use. The rockets were of 85 mm. diameter, and could carry a considerable explosive punch. The one-man launcher, about 4 ft. long, had the lightness of a rifle and the power of a cannon. Such a recoilless weapon was apparently mass-produced, and since that time considerable scale-up can be expected.

Now the United States has, of course, 57, 75, and 90 mm. recoilless weapons, but nothing (aside from the bazooka) is available in the small highly portable sizes of the Soviet hybrid AT weapon. And although the United States has investigated the solid fuel ramjet, for example, no actual operational weapons resulted. The United States took the road of developing a conventional atomic cannon; however, this proved to be too cumbersome operationally and fell before the advance of the guided missile.

On the fortieth anniversary of the Red Revolution, in November 1957, the Reds paraded two huge and apparently hybrid rockets through Red Square. Both were mounted on a heavy tank chassis and had very long barrels (of fairly light construction, though), with a relatively light recoil mechanism. It is suspected that both of these nuclear weapons were hybrid rockets. There were two distinct models.

One could have been a launching tube for the *Rheinbote* type of rocket. The Germans actually used this solid rocket late in the war; the weight was 3,782 lbs., it had four stages, and it could carry an 88 lb. warhead to an extreme range of 136 miles.

A launching tube with nozzle which could be relatively light (more so than a standard artillery piece of comparable caliber) could be provided, and accuracy could be improved. The 88 lb. warhead is now well within the realm of a nuclear warhead.

The other hybrid weapon shown appeared to be much lighter in construction and suggested a rocket booster solid-fuel ramjet. Range and payload would be increased over the conventional all-rocket weapon.

Cruise and hybrid rockets may now be obsolete in light of the big ballistic missiles. However, one word of caution: they probably exist in large numbers and are standard pieces of military equipment. These small-yield nuclear weapons pose a great threat for small, brush-fire wars. And they may also be in the hands of the satellite nations, Red China, and possibly in the Middle East also.

Nuclear Propulsion

At the present time we have no direct evidence that the Soviets have a nuclear airplane or rocket engine. However, it appears a distinct possibility that both are under development. As early as August 1955, General G.I. Pokrovski wrote about a nuclear turbojet engine. In 1957 a famous book *Applications of Atomic Engines in Aviation,* by Nesterenko, Sobolev, and Sushkov appeared, covering nuclear turbojets, ramjets, and rockets. One design presented showed an atomic turbojet engine of about 70,000 lb. thrust with a total engine weight of 33,000 lbs. (engine, reactor, and reflector). The engine had a diameter of about 90.6 in. and was about 21.4 ft. long. It was envisaged that two such engines could push an aircraft to a speed of Mach 3.6* at an altitude of 36,000 ft.; the entire aircraft would weigh 286,000 lbs. and could cruise 540,000 nautical miles on a consumption of 15 kilograms (33 lbs.) of uranium 235.

* See Technical Glossary.

In 1957 the authors Sinyarev and Dobrovol'ski wrote a book, *Liquid Rocket Engines,* and presented a detailed account of a nuclear rocket engine. Their performance calculations may be regarded as more hypothetical than actual. The reason for this statement is that they chose temperatures of 4,000 and 6,000 degrees Kelvin and working pressures of 100 atmospheres (1,500 psi.). Such conditions are believed to be clearly out of the realm of present-day technology. However, further along, one finds that the demands can be relaxed somewhat in a pile operating at 2,100 K and using uranium oxide and graphite. From such data, Table 7 gives specifications of their nuclear rocket engine while Figure 4 illustrates its size in comparison to the V-2 engine. This is a 250 metric ton thrust engine. It is interesting to speculate on what can be done with such an en-

TABLE 7
SOVIET NUCLEAR ROCKET ENGINE CHARACTERISTICS
250 METRIC TON THRUST

Parameter	Value
Thrust, sea level, lbs.	550,000
Thrust, vacuum, lbs.	620,000
Throat diameter, in.	17.35
Exit diameter, in.	77.6
Reactor diameter, in.	113
Reactor length, in.	113
Nozzle length, in.	138
Reactor plus nozzle length, in.	251
Operating pressure, psi.	1,470
Propellant flow rate, lb./sec.	1,166
Nuclear fuel	UO_2
Working fluid	H_2 (liquid hydrogen)
Moderator	C (Graphite)
Average core temp., F.	3,142
Gas exit temp., F.	2,942
Reactor power, MW.	13,200
Specific impulse, sea level, sec.	472
Specific impulse, vacuum, sec.	532

Soviet nuclear rocket engine (left) of
500,000 lb. thrust, compared with original
German V-2 rocket engine of 56,000 lb.
thrust. One such nuclear rocket engine could
carry 43½ tons in a 300 nautical mile orbit! It
would take several megapound-thrust chemical boosters to do the same job.

Figure 4

gine. Assuming a gross takeoff weight of 400,000 lbs., this 250
MT engine could orbit 43.5 tons in a 300 mile (nautical) orbit.
The useful load which can be placed into orbit is around 3,000
lbs. However, it should be remembered that the United States
Saturn, a three-stage chemical rocket, would be able to place
only one-half of this payload into orbit with its much greater
booster launching thrust of 1.5 million lbs. Thus, the great advantage can be seen in obtaining a high propellant specific impulse.

Future Propulsion Methods

Further out on the Soviet space science limb are descriptions
of all kinds of futuristic propulsion methods. These range from

Plate I—Ziolkovsky was honored by this issue a few days before the launching of Sputnik I.

Soviets Show Strong Link with Rockets and Space Flight in Their Postage Stamps

Plate II—Lenin is associated with such dynamic activities as rockets.

Plate III—Czechoslovak stamp pictures carrier rocket of Sputnik II.

SATELLITE STAMPS SHOW SATELLITES

Plate IV—Mongolia showed the other side of the moon as pictured by Lunik III.

Plate V—A. A. Blaganravov points to model of Lunik III while L. Sedov (right) listens. Both are well-known Soviet space scientists. Photo was taken at press conference held in Washington, D. C., in November 1959.

(Photograph by author)

Plate VI—Marshal Mitrofan Ivanovich Nedelin, formerly head of Soviet Army Artillery, who was Marshal of Rocketry, head of the Soviet Missile Command, at the time of his death in October 1960, while on tour of duty.

Plate VII—Marshal Kirill Semenovich Moskalenko, new Marshal of Rocketry, succeeding Nedelin after the latter's death. (This is a 1948 photograph.)

Plate VIII—T-1 medium-range ballistic missile on parade in Red Square, Moscow, November 7, 1957. It resembles the American Redstone missile. The T-1 was developed from the German V-2 rocket.

Plate IX—Tank-mounted T-7A solid rocket parades through Red Square, November 7, 1957. Highly mobile, it can carry an atomic warhead.

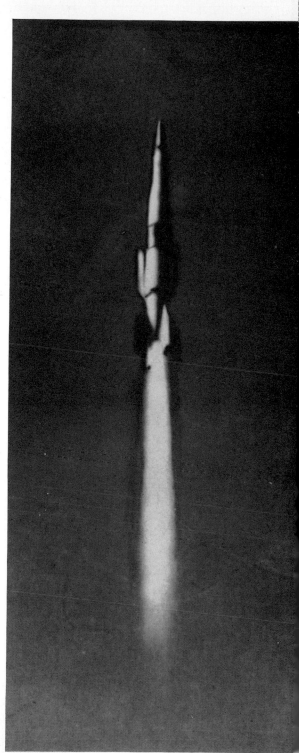

Plate X—Launching of a geophysical rocket. This multi-staged vehicle attained an altitude of 212 kilometers. Note pods on side, large fins on first stage, and frost-covered sides indicating possible use of LOX.

(*Sovfoto*)

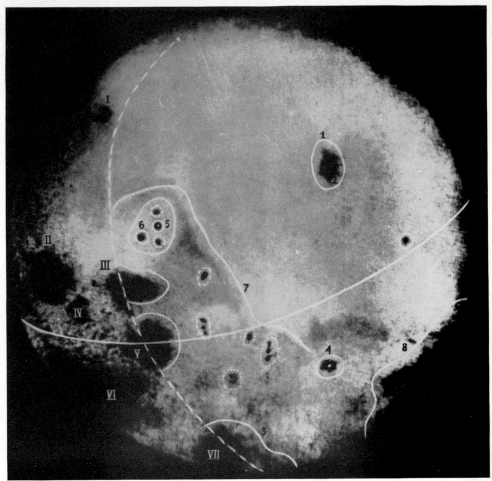

Plate XI—This unseen side of the moon was photographed by Lunik III. Soviet-named features are circled in white. Numbers indicate new features: 1. large crater Sea of Moscow, 300 km. diameter; 2. Gulf of Astronauts on the Sea of Moscow; 3. continuation of Mare Australe; 4. Ziolkovsky crater; 5. Lomonosov crater; 6. Joliot-Curie crater; 7. Sovietsky mountain range; 8. Sea of Dreams. Continuous line across surface is the moon's equator. The broken line at left divides the border between visible and invisible portions seen from earth. Features seen from earth: I. Mare Humboldt; II. Mare Crisium; III. Mare Marginis; IV. Sea of Waves; V. Mare Smythii; VI. Mare Foecundita; VII. Mare Australe.

the rather conventional views of the Westerners as ions, plasmas, beamed electrical power, and photons. On the other hand, wireless power rays and ball lightning have been mentioned. Thus, the Soviets are frantically scrambling around for new propulsion methods just as we are.

Future Soviet weapons have come under the close scrutiny of United States armed forces. In a statement to the Senate Armed Services Subcommittee on Military Construction, Brigadier General John T. Snodgrass outlined the next ten years of Soviet weapons:

A. 1961—United States under serious USSR ballistic missile threat.
B. 1963—USSR will rely on ICBM for its major delivery vehicle.
C. 1965—USSR will institute a military satellite threat.
D. 1966-1967—USSR will have operational hypersonic bombers (boost-glide or satellite type).

World War III

Aside from any small war, the implications of all this vast array of missile hardware would be most telling in any World War III. It is not the purpose of this section to speculate on the possibilities of any such outbreak. However, we should recognize, in the light of what is known or possible in terms of physical hardware, what these implications might mean to us in a hypothetical World War III.

First, as the destructive force grows with each weapon, it becomes possible to reduce conventional armaments, at least to some extent. Thus, it would be far easier to launch a surprise missile attack (even on a global basis) than it would have been to launch a blitzkrieg attack on a single nation during World War II. Missile bases are scattered and far-flung. Troops maintaining these missiles are always under some sort of alert and it is possible thus for only a few key people to be in the know and initiate an all-out attack.

How might such an attack on the Western nations come? Well, for one thing, it would probably be a missile time-on-target blow. That is, for shock value, each payload is designed to reach all targets—whether they be near or far—at about the same time. Since the flight time of an ICBM is around 30 minutes for its 5,000 mile range, and since the IRBM covers 1,500 miles in about 15 minutes, it can be seen that a staggered firing time would be required. This kind of schedule would give the most security to the attacker and be the type least arousing the suspicions of the troops.

For an attack on the United States the blow would be something like this. A fleet of 300-500 submarines (both conventional and nuclear) are spread out along our coast lines. They fire both cruise and ballistic weapons. Say from Cuba, 100 IRBM's are fired. Then, from Siberia a fusillade of some 500 ICBM's is already on the way. Shortly after a strike involving say 2,000 missiles of all kinds, a fleet of turboprop and turbojet transports airlifts some 5-10 mechanized divisions to the continental United States to set up communications and transport roadblocks.

Simultaneously, missiles have landed on all United States overseas SAC and TAC fighter and bomber bases. In addition, Europe and Britain are subjected to a fusillade of say, 500 IRBM's and immediately, from within the USSR, a force of 100 fully mechanized divisions begins the push to the English Channel. Europe is occupied within five days. Africa and Latin America are given the choice to die on the vine or surrender.

Of course, the USSR would be hit by those bombers that were not caught on the ground and those that did manage to get through a thoroughly alerted Soviet line. However, all military forces would have been out of target areas. Civilians would have had at least one hour warning. And those who did get hit?

Well, the Soviets have often said that they did not feel they would be totally destroyed by any Western attack. If the USSR would lose all of its unalerted and "superfluous" population? Not important, they would say. Via an alert, the most important people would avoid destruction because they would have moved from the target areas or managed to take shelter.

Now such an idea of "push-button" victory would have been scoffed at in years past. However, with the constant move of modern weapons technology, including the vast striking power of the ballistic missile, the dangers of such a victory loom ever closer.

CHAPTER 5

THE SPUTNIKS

THE SUDDEN EMERGENCE of the Sputniks on the scene did much to shake confidence in a Western technical superiority attitude. True, there had been several prior shocks, but they were not quite so dramatic. The early Soviet explosion of an A-bomb years before its anticipated time, the sudden revelation of an all-jet air force, the explosion of a hydrogen bomb, and the rattling of ballistic missiles all had come before. However, they went unheeded by most Americans. The October 1957 launching of the first artificial satellite did much to reorient American thinking. We have already read about the preludes of this Soviet push into space and the extreme significance that it attached to this new, dynamic philosophy of coupling dramatic areas of technological fields to further its ideological aims.

Pre-Sputnik

As dramatic as Sputnik I proved to be for most Westerners, the Soviets had been methodically working with their hardware. Indeed, they had openly announced their space intentions long before.

On November 27, 1953, Academician Alexander N. Nesmeyanov (head of the USSR Academy of Science) spoke before the World Peace Council in Vienna, Austria and said:

Science has reached a state where it is feasible to send a stratoplane
to the Moon, to create an artificial satellite of the Earth . . .

This key statement, from one of the highest officials, signified
a general opening of scientific discussions on the heretofore
closed topic of space flight. Many articles on space flight began
to appear in 1954 in all varieties of Soviet journals, newspapers,
and magazines.

Evening Moscow on April 16, 1955 added fuel to the coming
rocket fires when it announced that the USSR Academy of Sciences had established a permanent Commission of Interplanetary Communications. The committee was to coordinate and
direct all work connected with the solution of space flight problems. A.G. Karpenko was listed as scientific secretary while
our previously identified Academician L.I. Sedov was to head
up the group. Among the leading scientists on the staff were
Peter L. Kapitsa (well-known nuclear and cryogenics expert),
V.A. Ambartsumyan, P.P. Parenego, and B.V. Kukarkin. It was
stated that the first task was to organize work leading to an
automatic space laboratory.

To further glorify its coming space activities, the presidium
of the USSR Academy of Science announced establishment of
the K.E. Ziolkovsky Gold Medal for outstanding work in astronautics. This medal was to be awarded every three years starting in 1957.

On July 29, 1955, the White House announced that the
United States would develop and launch an earth satellite for
participation in the forthcoming IGY (International Geophysical Year).

Shortly after the American statement, Professor Kirill Stan-
yukovich of the Commission on Interplanetary Communications
praised the United States intention but stated that the USSR
would build its satellite bigger and better. He stated that a

three-stage rocket might be used to launch such a Soviet satellite.

Before Sputnik, as mentioned in Chapter 3, there was an unusual flurry of Russian activity which even included scientific visits to the various technical meetings in the Western world.

Another indication that something big was in the wind should have come from the First International Congress on Rockets and Guided Missiles in Paris, France, December 3-8, 1956. Two important papers were presented by the Soviets: "Study of the Upper Atmosphere by Means of Rockets at the USSR Academy of Science" by B.A. Mirtov and S.M. Poloskov; and "Study of the Vital Activity of Animals during Rocket Flight in the Upper Atmosphere" by A.V. Pokrovsky, director of the USSR Institute of Experimental Aeromedicine.

Poloskov and Mirtov described the use of high-altitude sounding rockets (weighing 250 kg., or over 500 lbs., and 2 meters long and 0.4 meters in diameter). Atmospheric composition data were obtained at altitudes of 80-95 km., pressures to 50-110 km., and wind speed and direction at 60-80 km. Other work was reported on recording UV (ultraviolet) radiation, solar corpuscular radiation, and micrometeorites. It was stated that the pressure measurements of the upper atmosphere pretty well agreed with the results obtained by United States researchers.

The paper of Pokrovsky on animal tests was later to prove of extreme interest in relation to Sputniks II and V. Single-stage rockets (similar in size and appearance to the V-2) carried large packages to altitudes of about 100 kilometers (over 60 miles). Then the packages were jettisoned from the rocket. Animal reactions were recorded on film. One film shown by the Russians revealed a brief glimpse of the carrier rocket and showed it to be an almost direct copy of the German V-2! Instrument packages were relatively crude (at least by American standards) along with the recording photo techniques. The films were usually quite grainy and often an ordinary wrist watch served as a time recording device. Women doctors and technicians appeared to be in charge of caring for the animals before and after launch. Later Pokrovsky said that the dogs were placed in special capsules and used space suits. The first stage of the tests was carried on with 9 dogs, several animals having made two flights. Accelerations were limited to about 5 G. Tests indicated no change in the animals. The sealed cabin provided protection for 3 hours while the space suits gave protection for 2 hours. The second stage of tests was carried out with 12 dogs and altitudes of the individual shots were between 100 and 110 kilometers. During rocket flight, the animals showed moderate changes in blood pressure, respiration, and pulse rate. Coasting flight indicated the same or very slightly reduced pulse rates. The following conclusions were reached:

1. Space suit tests proved that life can be sustained during rocket flights to 110 km., ejection and parachute descent from 85 km. to the ground, and free fall from altitudes of 50-35 km. to 4 km.

2. Animals could be ejected from the rocket at speeds of 700 meters per second and altitudes of 75-85 kilometers; or at speeds of 1,000 to 1,150 meters per second and altitudes of 35-50 kilometers, and successfully recovered.

3. In a space suit, animals could be successfully parachuted from altitudes of 75-85 kilometers.

4. Short flights (about an hour or so) do not have any physiological effects on animals in the upper atmosphere.

The significance of these tests was later evident in Sputnik II. Also, it is believed that the attempted return of Sputnik IV and the successful return of Sputnik V are all based on these early development programs. The successful orbiting of Sputnik V with its animals now indicates that man can do the same. There can be no question that the Soviets will shortly attempt to put a man into orbit and return him safely.

When the Russians were asked about the dog tests at a press conference at the Washington ARS meeting (December 1959), they said that they were using dogs in place of other animals or the primates because they were easier to train. Since the dogs were all female, it was asked if this meant that woman would be a Soviet astronaut. No, said the Russians, smilingly, the analogy did not hold!

Sputnik I

On Friday, October 4, 1957, Radio Moscow read the following announcement as issued by Tass, the Soviet News Agency:

For several years scientific research and experimental design work have been conducted in the Soviet Union on the creation of artificial satellites of the earth.

As already reported in the press, the first launching of the satellites in the USSR was planned for realization in accordance with the scientific research program of the International Geophysical Year.

As a result of very intensive work by scientific research institutes and design bureaus the first artificial satellite in the world has been created. On October 4, 1957, this first satellite was successfully launched in the USSR. According to preliminary data, the carrier rocket has imparted to the satellite the required orbital velocity of about 8000 meters per second. At the present time, the satellite is describing elliptical trajectories around the earth and its flight can be observed in the rays of the rising and setting sun with the aid of very simple optical instruments (binoculars, telescopes, etc.).

Then, the broadcast went on to give the few technical details that have been released. The maximum altitude was up to 900 kilometers and one complete revolution required one hour and thirty-five minutes. The satellite was described as being spherical in shape, weighing 83.6 kilograms, and transmitting signals at 20.005 and 40.002 megacycles per second (wave lengths of about 15 and 7.5 meters, respectively). Earlier, IGY had set aside the higher frequencies for tracking satellites and thus there was a mad scramble on the part of United States researchers to follow Sputnik at the lower frequencies. This American eagerness to track the satellite was marked by spontaneity and enthusiasm that had seldom been evidenced in science. The Soviets made sure that the transmitter had enough power and was of such a frequency that it could be picked up by radio amateurs. Thus, the Soviets scored another coup. Signals of about 0.3 second's duration gave rise to the familiar "beep, beep, beep" sound. Tracking stations, it was said, were set up in the Soviet Union. It was stated that 66 optical observation stations and 26 DOSAAF clubs with radio tracking equipment had been set up in the USSR to follow Sputnik. Thousands of radio amateurs were also helping.

However, since the density of the upper atmosphere at Sputnik's altitudes was not known, it was not known for sure how long Sputnik I would be in orbit. It was stated, though, that because of the great speed, the vehicle would eventually burn up in the atmosphere at an altitude of several "tens of kilometers."

Then, the Soviets went on to praise the pioneering work of Ziolkovsky and how this event would contribute to the world's science and culture. During the IGY, Russia said, it would launch several more even larger and heavier satellites. The Soviets did not give carrier rocket details. They said only that the greatest difficulties lay in the development of the carrier rocket, that powerful new engines working under difficult thermal conditions had been created, and that the rocket had achieved the necessary degree of reliability. In addition, a very precise automatic guidance system was claimed.

Concluded Radio Moscow:

Artificial earth satellites will pave the way to interplanetary travel and, apparently, our contemporaries will witness how the freed and conscientious labor of the people of the new socialist society makes the most daring dreams of mankind a reality.

The shocking size of the first satellite had three primary effects in the United States:

1. It proved that the USSR had huge booster rockets and led

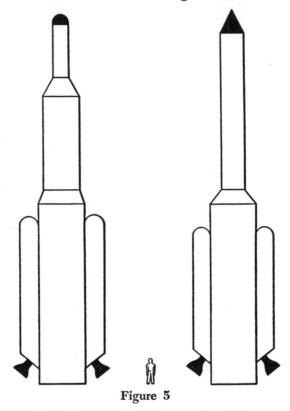

Figure 5

Possible configurations for Lunik (l.) and Sputnik (r.)

to the belief that ICBM's were being used.

2. It placed much tension on the United States Vanguard program—so much so that America's first satellite launch attempt ended in an ignominious ignition on December 6, 1957.

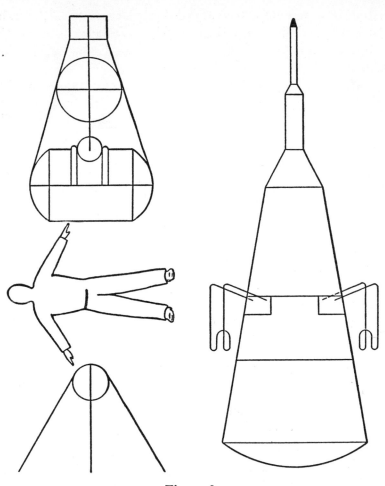

Figure 6

Growth of Sputniks is shown with Sputnik I (top l.), Sputnik II
(top r.), and below, Sputnik III.

3. A "crash" program go-ahead was given to the von Braun team to launch the Explorer satellite in 90 days.

Sputnik I (Sputnik means "earth satellite" or literally "fellow traveler") was launched on October 4, 1957 at 5:05 EDT. It carried the IGY designation 1957 Alpha.

Only very rudimentary information was released concerning the satellite. Some of the data are tabulated in Table 8. The Russians gave no information about the launching vehicle. Figure 6 shows, to scale, a lineup of all three Sputniks.

In order to carry a 184.3 lb. payload to the orbit at around 588 miles, United States experts figured that it required a rocket vehicle of about 200,000 to 300,000 lbs. and therefore considered that the Soviets were using an ICBM as a launching vehicle. Figure 5 gives an impression of the Sputnik (and Lunik) launching vehicles. A recent study of the design of step rockets has led to the belief that Sputnik was a two-staged rocket and did not have three stages as was popularly supposed. The large size of the carrier rocket has been determined to be at least on the order of 50-55 ft. long. It is here interesting to note that this is about the length of the T-1 ballistic missile. Tracking data giving the diameter of the last-stage rocket is somewhat more nebulous. It is believed to be around 5 ft., however, and this would again put it in the T-1 category. Even more interestingly, the power plant and shell of the German V-2 weighed 3,685 lbs. Lunik's last stages are reported to have been 3,324 lbs. for Lunik II and 3,423 lbs. for Lunik III. This, then, probably indicates again that a T-1, or modification thereof, was used as the last stage. The Soviets still report Sputnik I's launcher as a three-stage rocket.

Despite this perhaps important but for the time being unresolved question, it is presently very disconcerting to know that the Soviets have put into orbit around the earth and into deep space, last-stage packages as big as the V-2. One should not be confused by the Project Score (Atlas) satellite successfully launched by the United States on December 18, 1958, which put a total weight of 8,750 lbs. (the entire empty Atlas) into orbit but the scientific instrumentation (payload) amounted to only 150 lbs.

Sedov himself commented on the relative merits of Sputnik and Score. Sedov said that the United States had lumped together its carrier rocket weight with its payload weight. Continuing, he said that taking a ratio of 60 (as in the United States satellites) between payload and carrier rocket weight, the Soviet satellite's weight must have been 78 tons. However, he added that the Soviets had a much better ratio than this and that the total weight was under 78 tons but over the four empty tons of the Atlas.

Calculations indicate that a suitably designed T-2 (possibly with two solid boosters) could orbit a total load of 3,500 lbs. Actually, Sputnik put some 3,000 lbs. in orbit on later flights. However, a three-stage carrier rocket with two solid boosters has also been postulated for later vehicles such as Lunik.

With the launching of Sputnik I, Soviet prestige reached an all-time high. As a matter of fact, at the eighth IAF meeting in Barcelona the usually stone-faced Sedov is said to have offered an American scientist some instrument-package space on the next Sputnik! The Soviets were predicting bigger and better satellites. As a matter of fact, Sputnik I was stated to be merely a trial satellite for the IGY! The next shocker was to come shortly in Sputnik II.

Despite the limited amount of information the Soviets gave out on Sputnik I, the Western world managed to make its own interesting and valuable observations of this chunk of metal hurled into the sky. Some of the results are given below. Others are still in the process of evaluation.

Data of Millstone Radar, at the Lincoln Laboratory of MIT some miles northwest of Boston, gave a radar cross section of

120 square meters for vertical polarization (440 Mc/sec. @ 20 kw.).

The Jodrell Bank Radio Astronomy Station at Manchester, England with its 250 ft. radio telescope also covered radar reflection (in the 36-100 Mc/s range) and obtained the first contacts from Sputnik I on October 11, 1957. There was a signal fading due to rotation of the satellite, Faraday rotation, and ionospheric scintillation.

The Stanford Research Institute radars at Palo Alto, Calif., and College, Alaska, studied the Sputniks with 50 kw. radar (61 ft. parabolic reflector). The frequency was 106.1 Mc. and its minimum detectable radar cross section was 0.32 square meters for the instruments at a distance of 500 km. Sputnik I was tracked 13 times without obtaining cross section information. However, the results of tracking Sputnik II proved more productive.

The Jet Propulsion Laboratory at Pasadena, California, studied the modulation patterns of the Sputniks and catalogued radio signals. The pulse FM on analysis showed little correlation with geophysical factors. Data gathering was apparently on a global basis. An easily identifiable modulation was chosen and its telemetering capabilities were severely limited, JPL reported. JPL concluded that the modulation was intended first as a tracking signal and second as a measuring telemeter (with low information rate) particularly on fade patterns of 20 and 40 mc. Sputnik I did much to give the United States experience in tracking; these techniques were later applied to American satellites. JPL also picked up the rather surprising propagation effect through the earth's atmosphere. For example, the intensity of the Sputnik I signal was as great at a distance of 730-2,000 miles from the receiver as when it was directly overhead. There was, further, a daily fluctuation in this peaking effect. These peaks were attributed to reflections between the earth and the ionosphere and the existence of several frequencies within the peaks was attributed to reflection modes being superimposed which were due to the variation of electron density with altitude.

Nikita Khrushchev, backed by the USSR Academy of Science, charged that the casing of Sputnik I landed in Alaska. Robert Jastrow, then of the United States Naval Research Laboratory and now with NASA, however, delivered an IGY paper on the tracking of Sputnik I, and showed that this rocket actually landed in Outer Mongolia.

Sputnik II

About a month after the launching of the first artificial satellite of the earth, the Soviets upped the payload and put the first living animal into orbit! Purposes, according to the Soviets were:

1. to investigate the upper layers of the atmosphere
2. to study the physical processes of life in cosmic space

Although it was nicknamed "Muttnik" or "Dognik" by wags, the name Sputnik II has stuck. Dr. Teller, however, had a much more wry comment on the state of affairs: "We are so behaving that without any doubt, we shall stay ahead of the Russians in football." When Teller, father of the H-bomb, was asked what we would find on the moon he quipped: "Russians!"

Sputnik II was launched on November 3, 1957 and carried the IGY designation, 1957 Beta.

Radio Moscow announced:

The Soviet Union has launched the second artificial satellite. This time the satellite is carrying a dog in its cosmic flight. The second satellite weighs six times more than the first.

Sputnik II weighed 1,120.29 lbs., according to the Soviets, and contained a small capsule with the dog Laika (meaning "little barker") sealed inside an air-conditioned chamber. The dog breed is relatively small and is similar to the Spitz. Food and air were provided. Instruments measured respiration, blood temperature and pressure, and heartbeats. Other non-canine instrumentation measured solar UV, X, and cosmic radiation, plus external temperatures and pressures.

The United States also monitored Sputnik II's signals. Tracking was accomplished. A team at the Air Force Missile Development Center (Holloman Air Force Base near Alamagordo, New Mexico) picked up the signals but were not immediately able to decode them. A navy official estimated that some three months would be needed to decode telemetry data.

The USSR did not give its key to telemetry signals, either. To this date, decoded information has not been provided or made available. The Soviet scientists have always claimed that they do not give out raw or preliminary data; they would, however, present finished results in due time.

The big payload—over half a ton—shook most people. This was some 50 times that expected of Vanguard and some 35 times that of the first United States satellite (Explorer I) which was to be launched later on February 1, 1958. According to Convair's Krafft A. Ehricke, Sputnik II's launching vehicle was of such a size that it could have put a 50-100 lb. payload on the moon with a total of three stages. However, he pegged Sputnik II as a two-staged vehicle and estimated the first stage thrust at around 500,000 lbs. and a second stage of 77,000 lbs. thrust (a souped-up V-2). Dr. Donald J. Ritchie of Bendix Research Laboratories, on the other hand, has estimated performance of the first two Sputniks on the basis of three stages. Engel and Boedewadt predicated the use of three stages for Sputnik I and four stages for Sputnik II. The opinion of the author has fallen somewhere between an estimated big liquid propellant booster (plus two auxiliary solid rockets assisting) and a souped up V-2 (or T-1) for a second stage. This would amount to 2½ stages. Table 9 compares some of these speculations.

Subsequently, Laika died in orbit, and apparently recovery of the satellite was never planned.

Western world tracking information about Sputnik II has also given some interesting results. These are summarized rather tightly below. Millstone radar gave a cross section of 500 square meters. Jodrell Bank data revealed fading of signals of 2-5, 5-15, and 5-20 sec. duration. Stanford Research radar tracked Sputnik II some 48 times; most often apparent radar cross section was 1 square meter though a high of 437 square meters was recorded (corresponding to a volume of 196 cubic meters). A tumbling rate of 0.2-0.5 cycles per second was also recorded. The ROTI (Recording Optical Tracking Instrument) optical tracking telescope at Air Force Missile Test Center (Patrick Air Force Base, Florida) indicated the total length of 79 plus or minus 5 feet. Diameter was impossible to ascertain; this information was obtained at a distance of 200 miles.

A year later, the Soviets showed their Sputnik II instrumentation. Photos showed solar radiation detectors, cosmic ray detector, and two radio transmitters. In general, the electronic equipment was very large and appeared to be fairly unsophisticated. Apparently there was little attention given either to size or weight reductions. The Soviets claim to have tracked Sputnik II via optical methods, by use of long-range radar, and by reception of telemetry signals.

At the IGY conference in Moscow in 1958, the Soviets presented some data on Sputnik II. However, many scientists held that the Soviets were withholding some data similar to that already published openly by the Explorer and Vanguard programs. One item not disclosed was that of the orbital elements. However, they did give information on solar batteries and cosmic radiation. Information on Laika was also given. During takeoff, Laika was frightened (the rate of heartbeat accelerated to three times that of normal) but was calmed after acceleration cease. In a state of weightlessness in orbit, the dog's movements and heart rate dropped back; indeed, the heart rate dropped three times lower than the normal expected conditions under prolonged weightlessness. The Soviets claimed that after seven days in orbit, the animal was automatically fed some poisoned food. The effects of cosmic radiation were unknown since the body was not recovered. During the same IGY Moscow meeting, they said that they were already working on Sputnik III and that this would be a "cosmic observatory."

In August 1958 the Soviets announced that they had fired two dogs to an altitude of 279.63 miles (via a single stage rocket with a payload of 3,726.45 lbs.) and safely recovered them. Firings were made from the middle latitudes of Soviet European territory.

Sputnik III

This 1958 Delta was launched May 15, 1958 and placed an estimated weight of 3,550 lbs. into orbit. And, for the first time, the Soviets revealed an extensive electronic tracking system which they claimed was used to follow Sputnik III. Compared with the other Sputniks, *Pravda* said, tens of thousands of pieces of data had early been assimilated. This is compared to:

Sputnik I, 60,000 electronic and 400 optical
Sputnik II, 12,800 electronic and 2,000 optical

Findings in December of the same year included:

1. Ion composition in the atmosphere (230-950 km. or 140-600 miles): Most ions are oxygen while atomic nitrogen accounts for only 3-7 per cent of the composition of oxygen. No molecular forms of nitrogen, moreover, were recorded.
2. At altitudes of 1,000 km. (620 miles), noticeable quantities of ions were detected.

3. Temperature of ionosphere electrons is higher than those of ions or neutral particles. This was a surprising development.

4. Intensity of electron gas field was also large and turned out to be 10–100 times that expected. Measurements were based on flux of two electrostatic meters.

5. Magnetic fields were studied for the first time and spatial distributions were obtained. A magnetometer was used. A magnetic anomaly was said to exist in the upper layers of the earth's crust in eastern Siberia.

Sputnik III instrumentation agreed to a large extent with findings of the Explorer satellites on cosmic and corpuscular radiation. Instrumentation, according to those who saw models of the Sputnik III nose section, was simple in the extreme. Observers were struck with the uncomplicated engineering, the comparatively elementary construction, and the lack of meticulous detail.

The guidance system was also quite simple. A small computer takes electromagnet orientation data from the nose section and also from the accelerometers from Sputnik's sides and computes a program; at the right orientation the stages are separated and Sputnik III goes into orbit with the protective nose cap released.

Even less information on Sputnik III is available than on the previous two satellites. Millstone Radar, for example, reports a high cross section of 1,400 square meters.

Sputnik IV

Despite conflicting reports about the possibility of a manned Soviet satellite attempt, it was generally agreed that the Soviets were quietly up to something big.

Blaganravov and Sedov at the Washington ARS Meeting dodged questions about when Soviet man would be in orbit.

They said that manned satellite flight would come when developments had reached the proper stage and when automatic instruments alone could no longer do the job. The Russian scientist, B.S. Banilin, subsequently said that the main task facing Soviet satellite flight was that of safe and successful recovery.

The animal-carrying rockets were preludes to the Laika satellite (Sputnik II). In August 1958, the Russians had sent two dogs aloft in a rocket to an altitude of 280 miles. The dogs and the scientific instruments, weighing 3,726 lbs., were recovered from this single-stage rocket.

With Sputnik III orbiting the earth for almost two years without meteoric damage, it was logical to expect that the next phase of the Sputniks would be means leading to manned satellite flight and subsequent recovery.

Then, on May 15, 1960, the Soviets launched Sputnik IV. With the largest payload launched by far (total weight of about 10,000 lbs. in orbit), the Soviets themselves said that this was a prelude to manned satellite flight and that a recovery would be attempted. The Russians said that a dummy astronaut was aboard. Original speculation was that a live person was actually involved. However, this rumor was squashed when analysis of the voice broadcasts made from the satellite indicated that a taped message was being used.

Sputnik IV consisted of two parts: a pressurized and heat-regulated capsule type of cabin and a satellite instrumentation compartment. One was designed to be detached from the other. It is interesting to note that the launching was coincidental with the ill-fated Paris summit conference.

However, attempts at recovery failed. The retrorocket was apparently fired at the wrong time. The result was that the satellite went into a new and further-out-in-space orbit instead of slowing down. The Russian news agency, Tass, reported that on May 19, four days after launching, an order was sent to the satellite to switch on its braking device. Because it fired (apparently 180 degrees out of phase) in the wrong direction, the speed of the satellite was increased and it went into a new and more stable orbit. The last report issued by the National Space Surveillance Control Center (United States) gave a perigee of 189 statute miles and an apogee of 412 miles with a period of 94.3 minutes. The last stage rocket case, however, remained in the original orbit of perigee 189 miles and apogee 222 miles and a period of 91.1 minutes. However, both the orbits were in the same plane. It was also evident that many pieces started to show up. Late in May 1960, some seven pieces showed up in about the same orbit as the satellite itself and these pieces took about 16 minutes to pass in review in their orbit.

It was predicted that a man could be expected in a future Sputnik once successful recovery had been made.

Sputnik V

On August 19, 1960, the Soviets launched Sputnik V. The five ton satellite was in orbit at an altitude of 320 km. (198.8 miles). Orbital period was 90.6 minutes. The weight of the ship was variously listed as 10,120 and 10,143 lbs. whereas Sputnik IV was slightly less, around 4½ tons. The first broadcasts did not say whether a recovery attempt would be made. The passengers were two dogs Strelka ("Little Arrow") and Belka ("Squirrel") and other forms of life. It was stated that the functions of the animals were being monitored by the used of a TV camera placed in the satellite.

Then, on August 20, 1960, the Soviets announced that they had returned the satellite safely from orbit. They said it had returned to a spot (not announced geographically) some 6.2 miles from a preselected impact site. A "thermal shield" protected the satellite on its trip back to the surface. Thus, after being in orbit 24 hours, having made 17 or 18 revolutions, corresponding to 434,980 miles, the first satellite carrying living beings had been successfully brought back to earth. Later, Moscow announced that the other occupants had been rats, mice, insects, and even a flowering plant. All, apparently, were unharmed by their orbital journey.

Drawings and photos of the Sputnik V payload section showed it to be about 8 ft. long and about 3 ft. in diameter. Two sections were housed in a conical nose fairing. The first package (roughly spherical) contained scientific instruments. Next came a cylindrical cabin holding the dogs and other life. About 4 ft. long, the diameter was about 2 ft.

Later the perigee was listed at 190 miles and an apogee of 210 miles, thus indicating a nearly circular orbit.

The IAF meeting was being held in Stockholm, Sweden at this time and A.A. Blaganravov told press representatives that a manned Soviet space ship would be launched in the near future. This was quite a change in attitude in less than one year.

Sputnik VI

Soviet Premier Khrushchev announced that he would be at the United Nations in New York in September 1960. Moreover, he would be there for "several weeks." On September 14, the Soviet paper *Trud* forecast a manned space flight attempt soon. Just before this, there had been a report that Soviet astronauts were sent aloft to an altitude of 60 miles in a ballistic missile and successfully recovered. Then activities seemed to pick up. For one, Khrushchev would come to the United States on the liner "Baltika." On September 15, 1960, the United States Navy reported Soviet missile tracking ships in both the Atlantic and Pacific oceans. This led to the belief that the time was near for a sensational space shot. Perhaps Khrushchev might bring a recovered Russian astronaut to New York if all went well. The "Baltika," however, docked in Manhattan on September 19. It

carried Mr. Khrushchev and a host of satellite nations digni-
taries, but no man from a space satellite.

Radio Moscow had for weeks been blaring forth about a
forthcoming day-in-history—September 27, but this turned out
to be no man-in-space day. At Glen Cove, Long Island, Khrushchev said that all was ready (the rocket and the man) and
that the space launching time would be determined by the
scientists. Weeks earlier a "mystery" satellite had been reported
in various quarters. The United States had no such satellites
and the Soviets did not say anything, either. One report stated
that the satellite was moving in an unusual direction and opposite from the rotation of the earth. It was photographed and
British sources stated that it could have been the first of a
Soviet anti-satellite satellite. It could be expected that the
Soviets would not look kindly on any possible United States
spy satellites and were working quietly to come up with an
anti-satellite capability.

Although he did not elaborate on details, United States Air
Force Brigadier General Don Flickinger (director of bio-astro-
nautics for the Air Research and Development Command) said
that the Soviets had attempted to place two men into orbit.
The capsule had failed to go into orbit and the men were "clob-
bered."

Dr. William Pickering, director of the Jet Propulsion Laboratory, Pasadena, California, also said that the Russians had attempted to place men into orbit but had failed.

According to the Italian news agency, Continentale, the
Soviets had a disastrous launch failure on October 21, 1960.
The blast killed a hundred persons. Among them were Nedelin,
Rocket Chief, Deputy Chief of Staff General Nikolai O.
Pavolobsky; and Deputy Chairman of the Atomic Energy
Committee Professor Dmitri V. Effremov. A similar report has
supposedly been made by the United States Central Intelligence
Agency.

Sputnik VI placed another batch of animals in orbit on December 1, 1960. Details released by the Soviets indicated that it weighed some 104 pounds less than Sputnik V (10,143 lbs.) which had been recovered. The weight of the new 5.06 ton satellite did not include the last stage, according to the Soviets. The perigee of the animal-carrying satellite was 116 miles and the apogee was 159 miles. This low altitude indicated that either the lifetime of the satellite would be limited or that a recovery would be attempted. At first, the Soviets made no mention of a possible recovery attempt for this satellite with an orbital period of 88.6 minutes. Passengers aboard included two dogs, Pchelka ("Little Bee") and Mushka ("Little Fly") and other animals, insects, and plant life. Information regarding the functioning of life aboard Sputnik VI was being sent on a frequency of 19.995 megacycles. The United States Signal Corps tracking station at Fort Monmouth, New Jersey, picked up the signals at 8:16 A.M. on December 1. According to Space Business Daily, the official name of the satellite was Korabl-Sputnik III; and if all went well, the next would be a man-in-space attempt with the code name "Chelovek-Korabl I."

Clearly, possibly because of previous failures or because of a new liberalization of astronautics, the Soviets were preparing us for any possible failures. Dmitri Martinov (USSR Academy of Sciences) stated that the vehicle would not be aloft long. Ivan Shevlyakov (Moscow Planetarium) pointed out that the Sputnik was orbiting at a lower altitude than any previous satellite. Then a few days later the Soviets for the first time admitted a failure. Sputnik VI, the report said, had "returned along an uncalculated trajectory and burned out." This indicated a failure of the satellite orientation system which was also the reason for the failure of Sputnik IV. It was probable that the retrorocket of the satellite fired when the attitude was wrong. The result was a push into the heavier part of the atmosphere at a steep angle. Thus, the satellite burned up.

TABLE 8A THE EARLY SPUTNIKS

Data	Sputnik I	Sputnik II
Launch date	October 4, 1957	November 3, 1957
Burnup date	January 4, 1958	April 14, 1958
Total weight in orbit	ca. 4 tons (unofficial)	ca. 4 tons (unofficial)
Payload weight in orbit	184 lbs. (instrumentation)	1,120 lbs. (instrumentation)
Dimensions	22.8 in. diam. sphere	not disclosed
Perigee (miles)	142	140
Apogee (miles)	588	1,038
Period (minutes)	96.17	103.70
Perigee speed (mph.)	18,000	18,000
Apogee speed (mph.)	16,200	15,000
Inclination to equator (degrees)	65	65
Notes	Experiments: temp., press., measure. Aluminum alloy shell, 4 spring loaded whip antennae: 4 ft. 10½ in. long to 9½ ft.	Experiments: cosmic rays, solar UV and X rays Test Animal: Laika temp. and press. Aluminum alloy shell
	Transmitter: (a) 20.005 mc. (b) 40.002 mc.	Transmitter: (a) 20.005 mc. (b) 40.002 mc.
	Chemical batteries for power	Both stopped on November 10, 1957
	Transmitter stopped October 22, 1957	Accelerations of this satellite lead to acknowledgment of solar influence on upper air densities.

TABLE 8B THE LATER SPUTNIKS

Data	Sputnik III	Sputnik IV
Launch date	May 15, 1958	May 15, 1960
Burnup date	April 6, 1960	—
Total weight in orbit (lbs.)	ca. 7,000 (unofficial)	ca. 10,000 (unofficial)
Payload weight in orbit (lbs.)	2,925 (instruments)	3,250 (instruments) 5,512 (capsule)
Dimensions	conical: 11 ft., 9 in. long; 5 ft., 8 in. diam. at base	not disclosed
Perigee (miles)	135	188 (191)
Apogee (miles)	1,167	229 (429)
Period (minutes)	106	—
Perigee speed (mph.)	18,837	—
Apogee speed (mph.)	14,637	—
Inclination to equator (degrees)	65.3	
Notes	Experiments: atmospheric pressure & composition. Positive ion concentration, satellite electrical charge, earth's magnetic field, solar radiation, cosmic radiation, micrometers. Aluminum alloy shell, folded dipole antennae & trailing rods. Transmitter: (a) 20.005 mc. (chem. battery) (b) 40.01 (solar battery)	Test of manned satellite capsule and recovery. Retrorocket fired while satellite was in wrong position and pushed capsule into new and higher orbit.

According to *Space Business Daily*, this now indicates that there will be a Korabl-Sputnik IV (Sputnik VII) before a manned attempt is made.

About the time Khrushchev left New York to return to Russia, the four Soviet missile tracking ships also made their way back home. It is not very likely that the Soviets will say anything about the attempt. However, there is good evidence that the Soviets tried and failed.

According to Ernst Stuhlinger of NASA's George C. Marshall Space Flight Center, Huntsville, Alabama, the United States could not duplicate Sputnik IV's payload capabilities even with the largest United States missile, the Atlas. As a matter of fact, various Western authorities believe that the Soviet man-in-orbit program would need a vehicle about the size of our Saturn rocket. A first-stage thrust of 1,000 metric tons (2.2 million lbs.) for the Soviet orbital vehicle has been proposed by S.B. Kramer of Lockheed Missile Systems Division. Two or three such boosters could put a 60 ton satellite into orbit. Mr. Khrushchev talked of such a 60 ton satellite which would be placed into orbit "like a train." It was predicted that the next manned satellite attempt would come in January 1961.

Sputniks: Fact or Fiction?

Are the Sputniks real? Are they just a hoax or are they really much smaller than the Soviets claim them to be?

First, the Sputniks have been photographed, tracked optically, tracked via radar, and even followed via their infrared properties. The "beep, beep, beep" of Sputnik I's transmitter not only was picked up by professionals and amateurs alike, but via radio ranging received figures similar to those announced by the Russians. And via radio sounding we know that the signals were coming from outer space and not from a trick radio station in the Kremlin! Therefore, we can safely say that this is not a Russian "trick" or some sort of optical illusion or mirage. It is real. Trickery would involve just as much technical effort as a bona fide rocket and probably more. Therefore the Sputniks cannot be shrugged away.

Second, could the Soviets be exaggerating on the weights and sizes of the payloads? Yes and no! All Western evidence on the payload and last-stage rocket sections agree with the Soviets' data. True, they could fudge on the weights. True, the payload rockets displayed could be mere models. However, most of our indirect findings and soundings appear to support what the Russians claim. And soon the entire folly of deprecating their achievements catches up with you. The Soviets can't put a dog or a man in a 23 inch diameter sphere. And all their rocket technology points to conventional practices to accomplish what they have already accomplished. True, they could have made some terrific engineering breakthroughs like doubling the specific impulse of a propellant combination, or really shaving weights on their rockets. Neither of these is compatible with what has already been done. Then, Sputnik I density (52 lb./cubic foot) is consistent with current avionic (aviation electronics) package practices. There is no need to swing over on the other side of the fence and claim the Russians to be technical heroes. Rather, it is much safer to say that they have used normal technology to accomplish what is possible within that framework.

United States–USSR Satellite Comparisons

Late in 1959 Dr. Homer E. Newell, Jr. (assistant director of space sciences or NASA) compared United States–USSR satellite findings. The Soviets had chalked up the following:

They put the first artificial earth satellite into orbit.
They were the first to detect a current ring around the earth.
They were the first to put an animal into orbit.

In contrast, the United States satellite program had made the following firsts:

We first discovered the Van Allen radiation belt.

Moreover, we were able to discover two zones in this belt.

We made the first use of a geodetic satellite (Vanguard I) which gave the first refined information on size and shape of the earth. The earth is actually slightly pear shaped.

We were the first to use an elementary communication satellite (Score).

By mid-1960, the United States had added two more scientific satellite firsts:

Two Discoverer satellites were ejected from orbit and subsequently recovered. Thus, the United States beat Russia in getting a satellite back from orbit.

An Echo satellite (a large balloon) proved the feasibility of long-range reflective communications by use of a passive vehicle.

By mid-1960, Russia (with Sputnik V) was the first to recover life from orbit.

What was the value of Sputnik? In an address to the Electric Club of Los Angeles on November 16, 1959, Dr. Eberhardt Rechtin of the Jet Propulsion Laboratory conservatively estimated that the cash return of the Sputniks on the Soviet world prestige market was about $5 billion. By spending an estimated $500 million on them, the Russians had been able to receive a healthy ten to one return on their investment. Other satellite investments will be even bigger.

It has been claimed that the United States is getting more scientific results out of its satellite and space efforts than those obtained by the Soviets. S. M. Greenfield, United States Air Force Directorate of Research and Technology), however, has pointed out one of our scientific difficulties: We have spent something like $200 million in collecting data for the IGY and so far we have spent $1.5 million in "reducing" or making it meaningful. Several months were required just to "eyeball" the roomful of magnetic tapes that had been collected from our Explorer III shot. Preliminary information has been published but the University of Iowa group was still at data reduction of Explorer III and IV (1958) and didn't know how long it would take to finish the job. This great task of data reduction may account for the apparent and long time intervals between major Soviet shots. The Soviets evidently want to keep up with the data and start on a new shot only when they have completed work on the last one. It is stated that the Russians are setting up an organization whose task will be to incorporate all new data as it comes along into a "handy five-foot shelf" of environmental data. Thus, space "history" is being rewritten and made available as fast as it is accomplished.

Space Law

For quite some time, the USSR had been hedging on the matter of space law. There had been proposals regarding extensions of territorial limits to a given altitude. Below this altitude, the nation should have jurisdiction; above this, space should be analogous to the free or high seas and under no nation's jurisdiction. John C. Cooper early suggested such a boundary. Andrew G. Haley modified this limit to the altitude at which aerodynamic forces could no longer be used. Ari Shternfeld, USSR author and international prize winner for the promotion of astronautics, in his book *Soviet Space Science* appeared to look down on this sort of proposal which would limit the progress of astronautics by artificial laws. A more technically sound proposal has been given by G. Vernon Leopold in cooperation with Allison Scafuri (Space Flight Committee of the State Bar of Michigan) which involved two-part jurisdiction based on orbital parameters. The pro-

TABLE 9   SPUTNIK CONFIGURATIONS

Parameters	Sputnik I (CH-9)			Sputnik II (CH-10)	
	A[1]	B[1]	C[1]	A[1]	B[1]
Payload wt. in orbit, lbs.	184				
Total wt. in orbit, lbs.	202[2]				
Stage 4:					
Initial Wt., lbs.				3,713	
Propellant Wt., lbs.				2,596	
Structure Wt., lbs.				645	
Thrust, sea level, lbs.					
Thrust, vacuum, lbs.				8,800	
Burn time, sec.				81	
Stage 3:					
Initial Wt., lbs.	3,443			15,730	
Propellant Wt., lbs.	2,596			9,900	
Structural Wt., lbs.	645			2,116	
Thrust, sea level, lbs.					
Thrust, vacuum, lbs.	8,800	77,000[3]		36,080	77,000[3]
Burn time, sec.	81			70	
Stage 2:					
Initial Wt., lbs.	47,993			60,280	
Propellant Wt., lbs.	37,070			37,070	
Structural Wt., lbs.	7,480			7,480	
Thrust, sea level, lbs.		264,000[4]			268,000[5]
Thrust, vacuum, lbs.	116,600		99,000	116,600	
Burn time, sec.	76			76	
Stage 1:					
Initial Wt., lbs.	279,213			291,500	
Propellant Wt., lbs.	187,220			187,220	
Structural Wt., lbs.	44,000			44,000	
Thrust, sea level, lbs.	466,000	451,000[6]	440,000[7]	466,400	528,000[8]
Burn time, sec.	82			82	

[1] (A) Engel and Boedewadt; (B) Dr. D. J. Ritchie; (C) Author.
[2] Includes weight of nose cone of last stage.
[3] One R-10 engine.
[4] One R-14 engine.
[5] One R-14A engine.
[6] Two R-14 engines.
[7] Plus two 99,000 lb. solid boosters.
[8] Two R-14A engines.

posal was that there can be no arbitrary or artificial boundary altitude. The question can be technically and legally set by the flight mechanics of rockets. Below a certain energy and direction level, the rocket will return to the earth no matter what its altitude may be (viz, United States Pioneer I and III). Above a certain level, the craft will either be in an earth orbit or will leave the influence of the earth. Thus, jurisdiction could either be national or beyond the realms of international law. The Soviets are apparently in favor of such space freedom. However, there is a disconcerting note in that the Soviets do not believe in the freedom of a satellite to spy or otherwise encroach on the privacy of the USSR. Unless these matters can be resolved fast, we might expect even more serious incidents than the U-2 with our up-and-coming "spy" satellites.

CHAPTER 6

SPACE PROJECTS

THE PERIOD from May 1958 until early in 1959 was one of Soviet astronautical silence. Three Sputniks had been placed into orbit and many people were predicting manned satellite flights or flights to the moon. It was apparent that the next planned group of three rockets was timed to coincide with important political actions and/or with the astronomical facts of life in mind.

Lunik I

On January 2, 1959, at around noon, the Soviets launched their "Mechta" or "Hope" or "Dream" moon probe. The instrument package (a conical type about 10 ft. in diamater and 20 ft. long) received a burnout velocity of about 24,500 miles per hour. It missed the moon by about 4,660 miles (at 9:59 P.M. EST) and continued on into an orbit around the sun. The miss corresponded to an error of slightly over one degree. The later, ill-fated Pioneer III was off by 3½ degrees and as a consequence it also failed. Thus, Mechta (or as it is now more commonly called Lunik I) became the first artificial planet of the sun—or the solar system's "tenth planet." On a 15 month orbit around the sun, the Lunik's apogee was around 214.75 million miles on September 9, 1959. Perigee was reached on January 14, 1959 and this was 91.5 million miles.

The lunar probe was apparently launched to coincide with the visit of Anastas I. Mikoyan who was then visiting the United States and probably also to commemorate the beginning of another Soviet seven-year plan.

It is not known with certainty whether the Soviets planned to hit the moon or merely to miss it. Within a few hours of the launching, the Soviets announced that Lunik would miss the moon by about 3,726 to 4,968 miles from its surface. This information was apparently generated by knowledge of burn-out velocity and attitude of the last stage. Feeding this information into a computer would give an indication of whether the rocket would hit or miss. Yet, the Soviets were probably prepared for a lunar impact. The payload was marked with a Soviet symbol, a pennant, and the inscription, "USSR—January, 1959" which all seemed to point to a lunar impact. In addition, the Soviets discontinued the use of the name Mechta and in its place have continued to use the name Lunik. On January 6, A.A. Blaganravov stated that the January 2 firing was the first Soviet attempt to launch a rocket to the moon. This apparently was an attempt to squash rumors which stated that the Soviets had, unsuccessfully, made some eleven to twelve earlier attempts to reach the moon. Reports had stated that the first lunar attempt was made shortly after Sputnik I went into orbit. Firings are said to have continued at the rate of about one per month since 1957. Several rockets were said to have contained warheads in an attempt to cause a visible explosion on the surface of the moon. Apparently these were mere rumors since the first and subsequent Luniks were highly scientifically instrumented and were not merely stunt in nature. Indeed, it is said that the Soviets sterilized all equipment aboard the Luniks in order that contamination of the moon would not result.

One of the main reasons given for Lunik's miss of the moon was either an excessive velocity or a guidance error which prevented placing the rocket in an orbit around the moon.

Again, the Western world was made to realize that the Soviets had a tremendous power plant, probably ICBM in nature, which could propel the large payload of 796.5 lbs. to the moon.

On January 6, 1959, the Soviets officially announced that the Lunik's function was to miss the moon and become the first new Planet of our solar system. Instruments aboard were designed to:

> measure the magnetic field of the moon
> measure intensity and variation of cosmic rays beyond
>   the earth
> register photons in cosmic radiation
> probe the "radioactivity of the moon"
> cover distribution of heavy nuclei in cosmic rays
> study gas components in interplanetary matter
> record meteoric particles
> give skin and instrument chamber temperatures
> conduct a sodium cloud experiment

In its early flight, the rocket released a cloud of sodium vapor. This sodium was ionized in the upper atmosphere and photographed by the observatory at Alma Ata in Khazakstan while the cloud was visible for a period of some two to five minutes.

Radio transmitters were reported at 19.997 and 19.995 megacycles (telegraph messages of 81.6 seconds duration), 19.993 megacycles (variable duration of 50.9 seconds for telemetering scientific information), and 183.6 megacycles for coordinate measuring and also for transmission of information. It is interesting to note that the United States also picked up signals at 70.2 megacycles and 212 megacycles. The Soviets never announced these frequencies. An American tracking station in Hawaii picked up Lunik's signals some fifteen to twenty minutes after launch on 70.2 megacycles while the vehicle still had not been identified by the Soviets.

A most detailed but as yet unconfirmed report was published

in an American aviation magazine about Lunik I. The vehicle, states the report, was designated as CH-10 and was intended to impact the moon. Gross weight was 352,000 lbs. and initial thrust of the three stages (plus two solid boosters) was 660,000 lbs. A digest of the details is given in Table 9. The report goes on to say that launching took place from latitude 47° north and longitude 62½° east on the northeast edge of the Aral Sea. Thirteen tracking stations (from Prague to Voroshilov) followed the rocket. Injection angle was 71 degrees off vertical. Inside the vehicle, a pre-programed, perforated tape was used for guidance and instructions, while ground-based radar gave fine guidance control which enabled the Lunik to come close to its target.

The ability to cut off the third-stage combustion came with an accuracy of 0.1 second. The entire 3,245.76 lb. third stage went into orbit along with the payload of 796.67 lbs. The report, which came from Bonn, Germany, stated that the CH-10 used a modified T-3A as first stage, a modified T-2 as second stage, and a third-stage rocket specifically designed for use in space work. All stages used LOX and a hydrocarbon with an exotic fuel additive. Oxidizer to fuel ratio was 2.4:1 for all stages. As stated, this report, though possibly near in its estimate, is to be regarded as suspect. However, the report does give some interesting aspects of launch sequence:

T-60 minutes	Rocket instrumentation checked. Propellant topped off.
T-10 minutes	Maintain checks on instruments, fuel tanks, vertical position of vehicle until firing.
T-10 seconds	Start nitrogen-driven gyros in rocket. Ground engine run-up propellant is fed in from external source. Pyrotechnic cartridge ignites first-stage engine.
T-5 seconds	Check to see that gyros are at full speed, turbines at full speed, booster rocket delivering 484,000 lb. thrust. Launching is automatically stopped if these

are not at rated conditions. From T-10 seconds to T-5 seconds, the firing can also be "scrubbed" manually by crew in bunker if instrumentation so indicates.

T-5 seconds   Tanks full. Main control station gets gross weight figure to computer. Cut external feed. First-stage tanks start feed.

T-0 seconds   If everything is normal, solid propellant rockets are ignited, retaining arms are released, and the vehicle leaves the pad.

TABLE 10   LUNIK I DATA*

Stage	Value
Stage 3:	
Gross weight, lbs.	24,160
Propellant weight, lbs.	20,900
Length, ft.	20.3
Diameter (base), ft.	5.3
Thrust, lbs.	99,000
Burn time, sec.	50
Burnout velocity, miles/sec.	6.98
Stage 2:	
Gross weight, lbs.	113,300
Propellant weight, lbs.	94,600
Length, ft.	31.4
Diameter, ft.	13.7
Thrust, lbs.	410,000
Burn time, sec.	55
Burnout velocity, miles/sec.	3.36
Stage 1:	
Gross weight, lbs.	184,000
Propellant weight, lbs.	167,200
Length, ft.	53.1
Diameter, ft.	13.7
Thrust, sea level, lbs.	484,000
*Total thrust, sea level, lbs.	660,000
Burn time, sec.	80
Burnout velocity, miles/sec.	1.0

* Two Golem engines of 88,000 lb. thrust were used as boosters, thus giving an additional 176,000 lb. thrust.

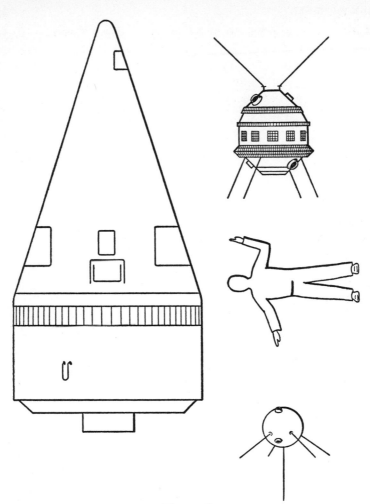

Figure 7

Lunik series has experienced a growth potential with Lunik I
(bottom l.), Lunik II (top), and Lunik III (bottom r.). Entire
nose cone of Lunik II is shown since size of actual effective payload
section is not known.

Table 10 gives a lineup of information about the three Lunik space shots. Figure 5, page oo has already presented a view of a possible Lunik configuration. Figure 7 gives a lineup, to scale, of the three Lunik payload packages.

There is at least one interesting implication of the large package sizes of the Luniks. Though the Soviets talk big about disarmament and have all kinds of idealistic and grand plans about outer space weapons bans, they continually fall flat when it comes to actual policing and inspection of such proposals. For example, with existing rockets, the Soviets could neatly test atomic and thermonuclear weapons in space with little or no fear of detection. According to A.H. Rosenfeld (of the Radiation Laboratory of the University of California), Lunik I, for example, could have carried a 500 lb. bomb past the moon. Then, by diverting a 300 lb. pack of sensing instruments (remember that the Soviets have already pioneered in such techniques) and a 20 lb. radio transmitter, they could have detonated an A-bomb in space which would be detected and recorded by the instruments and the data then radioed back to earth. According to Rosenfeld (in the book, *Fallout*), it would be almost impossible for unknowing earth stations to detect kiloton explosions beyond the moon.

From Nikita Khrushchev downward, there was rocket joy on the success of Lunik. The premier said that the Soviets "are the first in the world to map out the way from the earth to the moon" and that he, Khrushchev, felt "like hugging the man who has produced this, the first cosmic rocket, a new victory for the Soviet Union." Even Blaganravov began to talk; he said that someday the Russians "will walk along the edge of a crater of the moon, unravel the age-old secret of the canals on Mars, and see Venus unhampered by her cloak of cloud."

Unlike our Pioneer moon probe (Pioneer finally got into an orbit around the sun on March 3, 1959), the Lunik was high-powered enough (and had adequate guidance) so that it would either hit the moon or pass close by it and forever be rid of the earth's gravitational field. An indefinite lifetime in space is predicted for Lunik I. Two Convair scientists have stated they believe that it was the intention of Lunik to pass the moon and not impact it. The heliocentric orbit was planned, they say, and was to be a forerunner of a shot at Mars or Venus. The primary purpose, state these scientists, was to determine more readily the accuracy of the astronomical unit. This unit, now known only to four figures, is a relative yardstick for measuring astronomical distances and represents the distance between the earth and the sun. For space flight, an accuracy of at least six figures is needed. In other words, the earth is 1 AU. from the sun (80.7 million nautical miles or 149.5 million kilometers). At the present time, the mean error in the distance of the earth from the sun is known only to 15 earth radii. Margin in cutoff velocities then boils down to 33 ft./sec. And, for an earth to Mars flight, a departure error of 33 ft./sec. results in an orbital displacement of 40,000 miles. This corresponds to a speed error of about 22½ miles per hour. However, there is an even more serious error in flight time. For an error in arrival time of plus or minus 24 minutes for each foot per second of velocity, the arrival time error on a Mars trip would be 13.2 hours or in terms of an approaching probe, a distance of 0.6 million miles. Time and distance really hang heavy in space flight.

GUIDANCE

Soviet successes in putting vehicles into complex orbits and in coming close to predicted impact areas (such as the recent Pacific plunkings), now seem to indicate that Soviet mastery of guidance is just as good as ours. Guidance accomplishments can probably be attributed to the rather generous weights and volumes available for guidance in their relatively large rockets. And no need to spend years (as we did) in designing and perfecting complex, miniature equipment!

According to a recent Pacific Missile Range publication, the main Soviet launch site is near the Caspian Sea and this gives a range of 7,700 miles to a site near the Johnson Islands in the Pacific where two pairs of boosters were recently impacted. Another site, near the Aral, gives a range of 6,150 miles. From a site in Kamchatka, a range of 3,800 miles is possible. The Soviets put a total of four shots into the Pacific and these were believed to be space booster tests and not ICBM work. Indeed, the Soviets claimed that these were super-boosters being developed. A Czech publication recently said that the Soviet Cape Canaveral is near the shores of the Aral and is about 70 miles northeast of the city of Aralsk; this base is new and is devoted primarily to space work. In any case, the recent Pacific shots indicated that they could guide their vehicles over long ranges to within a mile or so of the intended target at ICBM ranges.

The following is indicative of the closemouthed characteristics of Russian guidance efforts. These comments were taken from the official transcript of the ARS press conference which the Russians gave at the Sheraton Park Hotel, in Washington, D.C., in November 1959:

QUESTION: Dr. Sedov, I wonder if there was any midcourse guidance on the lunar rockets, or was there any terminal guidance?

PROFESSOR SEDOV: After the end of the speed-up of the rocket, which was guided from the earth, no other guidance from the earth was performed. Only Newtonian forces guided it.

QUESTION: Professor Sedov, can you tell us if the equipment that was used to guide it, as far as it went, was electronic or mechanical or otherwise in nature?

PROFESSOR SEDOV: Will you repeat your question, please? I am not quite sure of it.

QUESTION: Was the computer that was used in the initial guidance up to the time of cutoff, electronic, or mechanical or otherwise constructed?

PROFESSOR SEDOV: On this first stage of the flight, the most modern means were employed.

QUESTION: Could you tell us what kind of modulation method was used in the transmission of data?

PROFESSOR SEDOV: This is purely a radio technical question, and the American radio technicians can answer this question better than I.

All questions were given to the scientists in Russian by an ever-present interpreter. The scientist in turn gave his answer in Russian to the interpreter, who gave it in English. It was obvious to both the author and others who knew Russian that, for example, Sedov understood the English question. This was most evident through actions and facial expressions when the sometimes embarrassing questions were asked.

The Soviets have claimed that their ICBM guidance system is capable of putting a missile on target with an error under 0.002 of the range. Ground stations for the guidance system are predicated.

Lunik II

When Soviet Premier Nikita S. Khrushchev arrived for his United States visit on September 21, 1959, he was armed with yet another propaganda victory. On September 12, 1959, Lunik II was launched, apparently intended for a lunar impact. The 858.44 pound payload hit nearly in the center of the moon (in the vicinity of the junctions of the seas of Rains, Serenity, Vapors, and Tranquility) on September 13, 1959 after a historic and propaganda-laden flight of 35 hours. The Soviets said that this impact was only some 125 to 185 miles from the intended target point. No rocket details were given and only the statement that it was a multistaged rocket. The last stage weighed 3,324 lbs. without fuel. This is highly significant as it is close to the structural weight indicated in Table 9 of this chapter and Table 8B of Chapter 5. In addition, it is close to the dead weight of the postulated T-1 configuration.

The Russians were careful to point out that they had decontaminated the rocket so as to keep the moon clean for any future scientific exploration.

The Soviets provided accurate tracking coordinates. The Jodrell Bank radio telescope was able to follow Lunik II for several hours. The Army Signal Corps, Fort Monmouth, New Jersey, was also able to track the rocket before impact.

Premier Khrushchev made it a point to state that there had been no failures prior to this shot.

A Professor Yuriy Krylov on Radio Moscow provided the only clues to the launching vehicle; he said that the "rocket is multi-staged with several engines in several compartments." He went on to indicate that several engines (viz., a cluster?) had been used. This incidentally coincides with the information previously hypothesized about Soviet configurations. Our friend Leonid Sedov stated that Lunik II's acceleration was limited to 1 meter per second, the angle to less than one degree, and the launch time to within a few seconds. The guidance system, stated Sedov, was common to all Soviet rockets and was used to control all stages including the final stage.

About nine hours after launch, the Soviet probe released a cloud of sodium vapor which was photographed by a number of universities.

The payload which hit the moon consisted mainly of two metal spheres, 3.54 inches in diameter. One sphere was made up of 72 pentagons (!) bearing the Soviet coat of arms and the inscription, "USSR, September 1959." In addition, a steel ribbon 12 inches long and ½ inch wide also bore the same inscription. It is believed that the final stage may also have impacted the moon; it carried a similar sphere like the instrument capsule but of 5.9 inches in diameter. The Soviets reported that the impact of Lunik II produced a cloud of dust and gas 310 to 560 miles high. The craters should be visible, said the Russians. If it hit a dirt layer, the probe crater would be 591 ft. across while the rocket would have caused an 853 ft. wide hole. On the other hand, if it hit rocks, the diameters should have been 33 ft. and 50 ft., respectively. No one has yet reported seeing a new crater on the moon.

There are many reasons why nobody so far as we know has yet seen the craters. For one, present telescopes on earth are not capable of resolving (thus being able to see or discern from the surrounding background) small craters. The best resolution of a ground telescope is on the order of one mile. And additional resolution difficulties with photographic processes would make it hard to prove small details on the moon. Final proof, thus, may not come until man actually sets foot on the moon!

Lunik III

The lunar triumvirate was completed with the successful launching of Lunik III. Launched on October 4, 1959, it was not until October 19 that the Soviets admitted that the probe's mission was to photograph the hitherto unseen side of the moon. Apparently this delay was due to the wait on the part of the Soviet scientists to see if everything was working as per design and the payload was on schedule.

The 614 lb. payload was a cylinder with hemispherical ends. It was pressurized and had two sets of antennae at either end. Both chemical and solar batteries were provided. The payload passed within 4,900 miles of the moon and continued on past it. On October 6, when at a distance of 37,284 to 43,498 miles the other side of the moon, a command from the earth started a 35 mm. camera taking pictures of the unseen side of the moon. Photography took place over a span of some forty minutes after the package had been properly oriented. The film had pre-

TABLE 11   LUNIK DATA

Name	Launch Date	Payload	Results
Lunik I	Jan. 2, 1959	Sphere: 796 lb. instruments. About 3,245 lbs. in orbit. Al-Mg alloy shell. Xmttrs: (a) 19.997 mc. (b) 19.995 mc. (c) 19.993 mc. (d) 183.6 mc.	In orbit around sun.
Lunik II	Sept. 12, 1959 (6 AM EDT)	Sphere: 858.4 lbs. last-stage minus fuel of 3,324 lbs.; 58.4 lbs. lunar probe. Dimensions not disclosed. Experiments: Temperature, pressure, magnetic fields of earth and moon, meteorites, cosmic ray nuclei. Al-Mg. alloy shell. transmitters: (a) 183.6 mc. (altimeter in probe) (b) 39.986 mc. (probe) (c) 19.993 mc. (probe) (d) 20.003 mc. (rocket) (e) 19.997 mc. (rocket)	Impacted on moon on Sept. 13, 1959, 5:02:24 P.M. EDT. Hit 1 minute and 24 sec. later than predicted. Total flight time ca. 35 hours. Last stage also impacted.
Lunik III	October 4, 1959	616 lbs. scientific instrum., last	Reached 4,373 miles from moon

(TABLE 11—Contd.)

Name	Launch Date	Payload	Results
		stage also in orbit. 3,423 lbs. with 345 scientific equipment. transmitters: (a) 183.6 mc. (5-20W) (b) 39.986 mc.	on Oct. 6. At 40,-000 mi. from moon, camera took pictures of reverse side of moon. Showed 70 per cent of moon's back. Camera operated on Oct. 7 for 40 min. Pictures processed and transmitted back to earth shortly before reaching perigee on Oct. 18. Now in highly eccentric orbit.

viously been protected from cosmic radiation. Developing and fixing of the special high temperature film took place under a condition of weightlessness and was automatic. When the probe started back to the earth, and when the Lunik was around 274,000 miles from the earth, the photos were electronically scanned (at a maximum rate of 1,000 lines per frame) and transmitted back to earth.

The Soviets later apparently constructed a composite photo mosaic of the moon's other side which was probably rephotographed to give the present familiar picture (Plate 10). Some 70 per cent of the unknown side was illuminated at the time and the photos also show 30 per cent of the area already visible from this side of the moon.

Merton E. Davies, a recon systems engineer for the Rand Corporation has recently analyzed the Russian photos of the other side of the moon. He reports that the photos are not fakes.

They may have been retouched, however. How good are the photos? Well, says Mr. Davies, the resolution is only around 30 miles. The best resolution of present ground telescopes is around 1 mile. At any rate, the photos should be looked on as a first view rather than anything refined.

When the Soviets released the moon photos, they already had named several of the more prominent features:

> Sea of Moscow
> Bay of Astronauts
> Lomonsov Crater
> Joliet-Curie Crater
> Sovetsky Mountains
> Ziolkovsky Crater
> Mechta Sea

Prior to this, astronomers had been trying to agree on naming lunar features by a numerical coordinate system. With the Soviets already starting a naming system on this unnamed side, it now seems that the "fresh" side is doomed to the ancient naming system like that employed on the visible side of the moon. For example, on the visible side, some 309 major features have been given names ranging from Abenezra to Zupus!

Other Space Projects

In 1955, Yu.S. Khlebtsevich described a robot space probe which was to land on the surface of the moon. Such a "tankette" laboratory was to be a small tracked vehicle which would have TV eyes and report back to earth about conditions on the moon. The 1,100 lb. robot tank would be soft-landed on the moon by the use of a 100 ton rocket (which had been refueled in orbit) or by using several vehicles without refuel. Putting such a package in a soft landing on the surface of the moon would indeed require huge rockets. Such a rocket would have to be at least the size of our Saturn booster combination but most probably about the size of the proposed United States Nova rocket.

A glimpse of such a cosmic rocket was provided in January 1956 by the Russian R.G. Perel'man (then a candidate of technical sciences) in *Nauka i Zhizn*. Figure 8 illustrates this configuration which uses a combination of ramjet boosters (for assist thrust while within the atmosphere), huge chemical clusters, a nuclear sustainer, and a smaller return rocket or winged variety. This huge rocket would be about 120 meters tall and would have a diameter of about 12 meters. It is illustrated in comparison to both the America's large and up-and-coming boosters, Saturn and Nova. All are compared in size with the United States Capitol Building.

The Soviets have already achieved a hard landing on the moon. A hard landing is defined as merely an impact with very probable destruction of the vehicle and/or payload. A soft landing, on the other hand, implies the use of braking (reverse) thrust so that the vehicle or payload gently touches the surface without damage. Thus, a soft landing may be next.

So far, the only data the Soviets have released about the moon (aside from the photos) is that it has no magnetic field to speak of. Thus, even a small package which might be made to survive a hard landing on the surface of the moon would be valuable if it gave information about temperature, pressure, and radiation.

What about a lunar landing by a Soviet man? According to a design analysis by a Lockheed engineer, the Soviets could put a man on the moon with a gross landing weight of about 3,245 lbs. (about the size of Lunik I). The rocket would be provided with retrothrust for a soft landing. Total payload capsule would be 794 lbs. (much smaller than that already achieved in Sputnik IV and V).

To return the man, a series of three vehicles would be sent

up. All this could be done with the small existing Sputnik and Lunik vehicles rather than by the use of the next generation "cosmic" rocket shown.

Of course, another "space shot" involving a human being could simply be the antipodal rocket concept. Neither a satel-

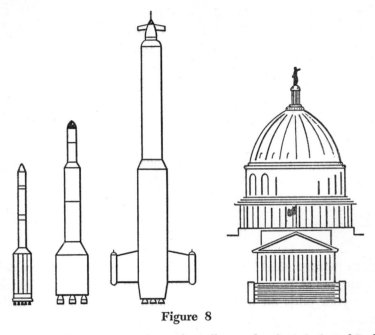

Figure 8

Coming generation of space rockets is here illustratad with U. S. Capitol Building serving as scale reference. From l. to r.: U. S. Saturn rocket (first stage cluster of rockets with 1,500,000 lb. thrust) due to be flown in 1961 or 1962; U. S. Nova rocket (cluster of 1,500,000 lb. thrust engines) to be ready later in the sixties; and a USSR "cosmic" rocket consisting of huge chemical clusters, nuclear sustainer, and a winged return rocket, ready time unknown but probably in the sixties.

lite nor a vertical probe, this could follow the patterns of the T-4A. Maximum range would be 9,936 miles.

Other space programs postulated and speculated on by United States observers include a number of interplanetary

flights. Mars and Venus are the ones most likely for the near
future.

For those who would like to keep their own score (and possibly place a few wagers), here are the most favorable launching dates (some of them past) for Earth-to-Mars trips:

> October 1, 1960
> November 16, 1962
> December 23, 1964
> January 26, 1967
> February 28, 1969

while for Earth-to-Venus jaunts:

> June 8, 1959
> January 13, 1961
> August 16, 1962
> March 28, 1964
> October 27, 1965
> June 5, 1967

where astronomical facts of life give the lowest launch velocity
requirements. However, if the Soviets can afford larger vehicles,
then your odds on using these dates and coming up with a
winner are very poor.

The Soviets are already talking about the use of several
"transit" or refueling space stations for trips to the moon and
other planets.

Figure 9 presents an over-all view of present and possible
space ventures. First came the unmanned Sputniks and Luniks.
Next will come manned orbital flight, deeper space probes, and
finally, manned landing on the moon. These statements come
from the Russians themselves. As announced by the USSR
Academy of Science, the long-range space program shapes up
something like this:

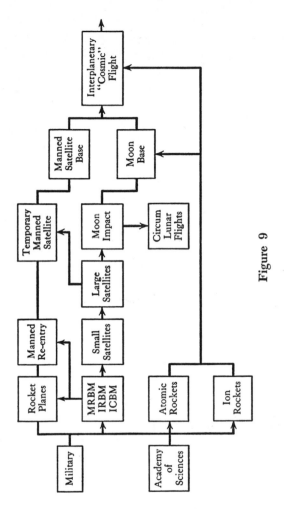

Figure 9

Diagram of Soviet space program. Many of the items at left top have been accomplished and it can be seen how early developments hinged on military rockets. Future accomplishments will be atomic and ion rockets, but first the second generation of huge chemical rockets now under development. Ultimate goals: a Soviet-manned solar system!

long-term satellites
recoverable satellites
manned earth satellites
flight to the moon and other planets
high apogee satellites
interplanetary space stations which can be manned for
    long durations
manned flight to Mars and Venus

For example, V. Petrov specifically outlines Soviet aims in the near future as:

unmanned earth satellites
manned satellites
unmanned rocket around the moon
manned rocket landing on the moon

followed by visits to the other planets of the solar system.

As Ziolkovsky said in 1913: "Mankind will not stay on the Earth forever, but in the pursuit of world space, will at first timidly penetrate beyond the limits of the atmosphere and then will conquer all the space around the sun," and in another statement: "The earth is the cradle of the mind, but one cannot live forever in a cradle!"

It is certain that the Soviets are hanging their Red Hat on the White Stars!

EPILOGUE

THE WESTERN world was shaken by the achievements of Soviet space technology as perhaps by no other development. Although America has stepped up its efforts, we are still behind three years since Sputnik I was launched in 1957. Indeed, step by step, our superiority has seemed to diminish. First, it was acknowledged that the Soviets were ahead in the thrust department. However, it was stated, we were ahead in guidance. And the Soviets might have more powerful rockets than we but we still had better ones. The Lunik series and the recent impacts in the Pacific Ocean seem to have deflated our delusions of grandeur. About our only claim to fame is that our rockets are more sophisticated. The Soviets are doing the same thing, then, with simpler vehicles. Still, it is claimed, we have obtained more scientific information about space than the Soviets. Whether this is true is not known. The Soviets release only those data that they care to. And there is a good possibility that the Soviets have not revealed their more "work-horse" program.

Whether the United States can pull ahead in the future is also now unknown. America has organized a national space agency and outlined some tentative space goals. However, all are contingent on budgets, emphasis, and availability of a myriad of rival rockets. The United States needs a more powerful, long-range centralized coordinating group. As we have

TABLE 12   BOX SCORE—USA vs. USSR[1]
PERFORMANCES OF SATELLITES AND
SPACE SHOTS COMPARED[2]

| USA | | USSR | |
Name	Payload	Name	Payload
Explorer I	30.8	Sputnik I	184
Vanguard I	3.25	Sputnik II	1,120
Explorer III	31	Sputnik III	2,925
Explorer IV	38.4	Lunik I	796
Score	150	Lunik II	858
Vanguard II	20.74	Lunik III	614
Pioneer IV	13.4	Sputnik IV	10,008
Discoverer I	245	Sputnik V	10,000
Discoverer V	300	Sputnik VI	10,000
Discoverer VI	300		
Vanguard III	50	9 vehicles	36,505
Explorer VII	91.5		
Discoverer VII	300		
Discoverer VIII	300		
Pioneer V	94.8		
Tiros I	270		
Transit B	265		
Midas II	300		
Transit II-A	223		
NRLI	40		
Discoverer XIII	150		
Discoverer XIV	150		
Echo I	191		
Courier B	500		
Explorer VIII	90		
Discoverer XVII	300		
Tiros II	280		
Discoverer –VIII	300		
28 vehicles	5027.89		

[1] It should be noticed that the Soviets have put about seven times the weight into orbit and/or space than the United States. In addition, the Soviets have accomplished this sevenfold weight performance with about one-third the number of vehicles!

[2] This includes all vehicles successfully launched as of December 12, 1960. Does not include Soviet failures (which are not announced) and does not

seen, the Soviets are apparently working on a long-range program. The second generation of rockets appears on the horizon and will prove to be composed of greater shockers than Sputnik and Lunik.

What can the United States do? We feel that some drastic and needed steps can be taken. We should learn from our competitor across the ICBM pond. The following are some suggestions which should be construed as strictly those of the author.

First we should attempt to take some of the steam out of Soviet space accomplishments. It is generally known, for example, that our military and our Central Intelligence Agency get wind of future shots. The Soviets don't talk about their failures; ours, on the other hand, are well known. To cut the Soviets down to size we ought to make these failures known. And we ought to notify the public about our own important launchings before the Soviets make up their minds as to their goals. Therefore, a public information office should be created, say within CIA, to give a Western view of these important shots. Within security, these Western views should be presented to the public, and soon. These releases can strengthen our own programs. For obvious reasons such releases should be based on technological state-of-the-art and the office should not be merely a propaganda agency. It should be staffed and run by engineers and scientists.

Second, we need a reorganized defense setup. It should be realized that the United States Department of Defense serves one aim—to defend the United States and its allies. Therefore, it has one customer—the free citizen. Rival service groups do much to diminish our strength. There should, therefore, be

---

include those United States vehicles which we know failed. In some cases, United States payload weights have been lumped together with the total weight in orbit or in space. Therefore actual effective weight should be under that shown.

only one military group. It should have the same uniform and the same administrative and procurement setup, to save tax dollars. The unified group probably should be organized into four arms:

Army Force
Navy Force
Air Force
Space Force, or an Aero-Space Force

The Army Force, in addition to the more conventional aims, should control all ground installations (navy, air, and space). It is a well-known fact, for example, that some 50-80 per cent of a missile system's budget stays on the ground. Why not have it operated by a ground group? Though operation of an air base, a naval base, or a space base may have its pecularities, all have greater things in common. The Army or Ground Force should operate IRBM and ICBM bases. Think how ridiculous it is to have an Air Force group tending a hole in the ground! All land-operated missiles should be operated by the Army.

The Navy Force would pretty much be as it is now. The sea has its own pecularities, and ships and subs are the domain of the Navy. Such aircraft or missiles as are necessary for protection or offense of naval fleets should be the domain of the Navy without regard to range or size.

The Air Force should get back to the airplane—whether it be driven by props, turbojets, ramjets, rockets, or even a nuclear power plant. Range and altitude should be determined by the needs of the service. Armaments, whether conventional or missile-age, would be provided.

The Space Force would establish satellites and planetary missions as deemed necessary to defend the free world. All scientific or research rockets, space probes, satellites, and planetary missions should be handled by this one force. Though the military significance of a space force is yet to be realized, it probably will become commonplace in the world of tomorrow.

And, this central defense force should be the designer, developer, and constructor of all missiles and spacecraft. It should develop them and farm them out to the various arms as necessary. Now all the services are engaged in building bigger competing missile and spacecraft systems on their own and apparently with little coordination. It would be much better, for example, to have this central group develop a submarine launched IRBM, for example, so that with addition of another stage, it could serve as an ICBM to be used by the Army Force.

What of civilian spacecraft or rockets? With the present world situation, it is doubtful if missile weapons could be dispensed with. Military rockets are classified in this climate. Unless you can have absolute freedom of information, then there is doubt that civilian models can be made available. Even propulsion system data on our "unclassified" Vanguard rocket are not available to all. Also, the heavy costs of missiles and space systems will probably make them the favorite toys of large governments; no large private corporation could afford them. This is as it should be, under present views, since these items were developed by our tax dollars. Even those private rocket groups who claim to have developed a particular rocket "on their own funds" have done so by profiting from government programs and from a government-sponsored technological base.

Yet another item about our defense. United States policy about defense has been based on retaliation in event of a war. Very little has been done to make an attack on the United States a hazardous undertaking. True, we have a fairly good (but unproven) aircraft-oriented defense system. However, it looks as if the Soviets had early decided to by-pass the bomber and concentrate on the missile. United States civilian defense, organizationally, is poor and ill-funded. A shelter program does not exist. An operational anti-missile system does not exist. As

we have seen, the Soviets may intend to obliterate our re-
taliatory forces in any first blow. Therefore, the aim should be
to prevent (physically) such an anti-retaliatory blow. Thus
far, only the anti-missile missile seems capable of destroying
any possible enemy missile. As crude and costly as it is likely
to be, it is apparently our only salvation in event of an all-out
conflict.

And exploration of other planets and subsequent free world
occupation should tend to dull or dilute any possible earth
aggression.

Finally, in any new art, science, or technology, the leaders
of the new movement are hard put to explain the importance
of their venture. This applies to space technology. The leaders
are now mainly guided by a feeling or conviction that they are
doing the right thing and that the nation should back them.
There are scientific and technological supports for their claims,
but these are inadequate. One cannot always put feelings into
words. We ought then to make the decision that the United
States should be a leader in space and then pursue this aim
to the utmost with the least possible hampering tactics. Just as
the New World of today would have been impossible to describe in the times of Columbus, so now it is as hard to tell the
importance to America of the next century in space. Space
exploration is just as important as medicine, agriculture, technical aid, etc. Space is big and will be costly, but through
technology we can find benefits that are undreamed of today.
It is apparent that the Soviets so regard space!

REFERENCES

CHAPTER 1

F. J. KRIEGER. "A Casebook on Soviet Astronautics," U.S. Air Force Project Rand Research Memo., RM-1760, Rand Corp., Santa Monica, Calif., 1956.

D. J. RITCHIE. "Technical Development in Propulsion in the Soviet Union," Report No. 1212, Bendix Aviation Corp., Research Labs. Div., Detroit, Mich., 1959.

A. J. ZAEHRINGER. Solid Propellant Rockets, American Rocket Co., Wyandotte, Michigan, 1958.

H. GARTMANN. Traumer, Forscher, Konstrukteure. Düsseldorf, Germany: Econ Verlag, 1955.

CHAPTER 2

N. DeWITT. "Soviet Professional Manpower," National Science Foundation, Washington, D.C., 1955.

L. TRILLING in Aviation Week (Aug. 20, 27, Sept. 3, 10, 1956).

G. W. SCHROEDER. "How Russian Engineering Looked to a Captured German Scientist," Aviation Week (May 9, 1955).

"Education in the Soviet Setting," Chemical & Engineering News, (Nov. 25, 1957), pp. 76ff.

H. GRÖTTRUP. "Aus den Arbeiten des deutschen Raketen-Kollektivs in der Sowjet-Union," Raketentechnik und Raumfahrtforschung, Heft 2 (April 1958).

"Rickover Tells Why US Trails Russia," Missiles & Rockets, (May 9, 1960), p. 16.

Address to Electric Club of Los Angeles, Nov. 16, 1959, by Dr. Eberhardt Rechtin.

D. LAURENT. "Les Engins Speciaux Sovietiques," *Docaero,* No. 39, (July, 1956), pp. 3-12.

VOLURSUS. "Die Geheimwaffen der Sowjet-Union," *Flugwelt,* (Nov. 1955), pp. 349-353.

G. SUTTON. "Rockets Behind the Iron Curtain." Paper given on December 4, 1952, American Rocket Society, New York City.

CHAPTER 3

"Handbook on the Soviet Army," Dept. Army Pamphlet No. 30-50-1, Washington, D. C., July 31, 1958.

"Military Aspects of World Political Geography," 1959 Edition, AFROTC, Air University, Maxwell AFB, Alabama.

A. KRAMISH. *Atomic Energy in the Soviet Union,* Stanford, Calif.: Stanford University Press, 1959.

R. G. PEREL'MAN. *Soviet Nuclear Propulsion.* Washington, D. C.: Triumph Publishing Co.

A. PARRY. "Soviet Affairs," *Missiles & Rockets,* vol. 6 (June 13, 1960), p. 45.

W. F. KENNEDY. "Soviet Air Strength," *Ordnance,* vol. 43 (May-June 1959), pp. 911-914.

——. "The Red Army," *Ordnance,* vol. 42, (Sept.-Oct. 1958), pp. 227-229.

I. HEYMOUNT. "Soviet Ground Weapons," *Ordnance,* vol. 43 (May-June 1959), pp. 906-910.

J. BAAR. "Russia's Big Missile Bases," *Missiles & Rockets,* vol. 6 (Feb. 15, 1960), pp. 25-29.

G. UNDERHILL, "Soviet Air Transport," *Ordnance,* vol. 42 (Jan.-Feb. 1958), pp. 624-628.

H. F. MARK. "Soviet Polymer Science Today," *Modern Plastics,* vol. 35, (July 1958), pp. 111-186.

A. J. ZAEHRINGER, "USSR May Have Tested Atomic Rocket," *Missiles & Rockets,* vol. 4 (Dec. 22, 1958), pp. 13-14.

——. "The Soviet Space Race," *Ordnance,* vol. 44 (July-Aug. 1960), pp. 45-48.

"Soviets Reorganize Science Management," *Aviation Week,* vol. 71 (July 13, 1959), pp. 69-74.

J. W. USELLER. "Soviet Science," *Ordnance,* 42 (Sept.-Oct. 1958), pp. 242-245.

D. D. BAKER, M. HOSEH. "Soviet Science Information Services," *Chemical & Engineering News,* vol. 38 (Jan. 11, 1960), pp. 70-75.

R. E. MARSHAK. "Scientific Research in the Soviet Union," *Jet Propulsion,* vol. 27 (Feb. 1957), pp. 200-209.

A. G. HALEY. "Chinese Astronautical Research," *Astronautics,* vol. 5 (Feb, June, July 1960).

CHAPTER 4

A. J. ZAEHRINGER. "Soviet Missiles, Part 1. Liquid Rockets," *Missile Design & Development,* vol. 6 (Jan. 1960), pp. 38-40.

——. "USSR Plan: Sputniki for Sputniki," *Missiles & Rockets,* vol. 5 (Dec. 15, 1958), p. 17.

——. "Soviet Missiles, Part 2. Solid Rockets," *Missile Design & Development,* vol. 6 (Feb. 1960), pp. 26-28.

——. "Soviet Missiles, Part 3. Cruise Missiles, Ramjets, and Hybrid Rockets," *Missiles Design & Development,* vol. 6 (April 1960), pp. 29-30.

——. "USSR May Have Tested Atom Rocket," *Missiles & Rockets,* vol. 5, (Dec. 22, 1958), pp. 13-14.

P. MEANS. "Report Pinpoints Red Launch Base," *Missiles & Rockets,* vol. 6 (Sept. 7, 1959), p. 21.

"Russian Range," *Missile Missives,* No. 11 (Aug. 12, 1960), p. 3.

V. KRIKSUNOV. "Counterweapon Systems vs. the ICBM," *Space/Aeronautics,* vol. 34, (March 1960), pp. 151-154.

A. PARRY. "Soviet Affairs," *Missiles & Rockets,* vol. 7 (Aug. 1, 1960), p. 43.

——. "Soviet Affairs," *Missiles & Rockets,* vol. 7 (Aug. 15, 1960), p. 42.

B. G. WEINSCHEL. "Russian Test Equipment and Ours," *Electronic Design,* vol. 8 (Aug. 17, 1960), pp. 50-70.

CHAPTER 5

F. J. KRIEGER. "Behind the Sputniks," Public Affairs Press, Washington, D. C., 1958.

"Russian High Altitude Research," *Jet Propulsion,* vol. 27 (Feb. 1957), pp. 186-188.

D. J. RITCHIE. "Technical Development in Propulsion in the Soviet Union," Bendix Corp., Detroit, Mich., 1959.

——. "Soviet Rockets Exploit German Technology," *Missiles & Rockets,* vol. 6, (Dec. 7, 1959), pp. 17-19.

Avionics Research: Satellites and Problems of Long Range Detection and Tracking, edited by E. V. D. CLAZIER, E. RECHTIN, J. VOGE. New York: Pergamon Press, Inc., 1960.

R. ENGEL, V. T. BOEDEWADT. "Die Satelliten-Tragerraketen," *Raketentechnik und Raumfahrtforschung*, Band II, Heft 1 (Jan. 1958), pp. 23-25.

R. E. STOCKWELL. "Sputnik III's Guidence System," *Missile Design & Development*, vol. 4 (Sept. 1958), pp. 12-14.

H. E. NEWELL. "U. S., Russian Space Efforts Compared," *Aviation Week*, No. 72 (Dec. 21, 1959), pp. 36-50.

DR. EBERHARDT RECHTIN. "Who Says There's a Space Race?" (JPL), Presented to Electric Club of Los Angeles, Nov. 16, 1959.

S. B. KRAMER. "Soviet Space Shots," *Aviation Week*, vol. 73 (Sept. 26, 1960).

CHAPTER 6

"Soviets Hoped To Impact Mechta on Moon," *Aviation Week*, vol. 72 (Jan. 26, 1959), pp. 26-29.

Fallout, edited by J. M. Fowler. New York: Basic Books, Inc., 1960.

W. A. DALEY, D. H. ROBEY. "Mechta's Trip Past the Moon May Have Been Intentional," *Aviation Week*. vol. 72 (March 30, 1959), pp. 66-72.

The Other Side of the Moon, translated by J. B. Sykes. New York: Pergamon Press, Inc., 1960.

M. E. DAVIES. "How Good Is the Lunik III Photography?" *Astronautics*, vol. 5 (May 1960), p. 28.

———. "Are the Lunik III Photos Fake?" *Astronautics*, vol. 5 (June 1960), p. 46.

B. RISING. "How Soviets May Land Man on the Moon," *Aviation Week*, vol. 72 (May 11, 1960) pp. 54-61.

"Soviets Study 'Transit Stations,' " (Feb. 15, 1960), p. 31.

E. CLARK. "Soviets Prepare To Put Man into Space," *Aviation Week*, vol. 72 (Jan. 19, 1959), p. 26.

"The Next Ten Years in Space: 1959-1969." Staff Report of the Select Committee on Astronautics and Space Exploration. House Document No. 115, U. S. Government Printing Office ,Washington, D. C., 1959.

"Scientific and Technical Aspects of NASA Program," H. R. 10809, June 30, 1960, U. S. Government Printing Office, Washington, D. C., 1960.

TECHNICAL GLOSSARY

AA—Abbreviation for antiaircraft.

ABLATION—A process for protecting re-entering ballistic missile nose cones involving a gradual burning or vaporizing away. Usually using plastics, the top surface burns away but the inner masses remain cool. A very efficient process for one-shot vehicles.

ACTIVE—Usually applied to guidance systems and indicating that the system is carried within the vehicle and performs its own functions.

ANTIPODAL—Applied to a vehicle that can travel halfway around the earth. Since the circumference of the earth is around 25,000 miles, the range of an antipodal rocket would be about 12,000 miles.

APOGEE—That point on an orbit or trajectory which is the greatest distance away.

ARS—American Rocket Society.

ASTRONAUTICS—The science and art of space travel.

ASTRONAUTICAL UNIT—Abbreviation is AU. Equal to the distance from the earth to the sun, around 93 million miles.

AZIMUTH—An arc of the horizon measured clockwise between a fixed point and the vertical circle passing through the center of an object. (Merriam Webster.)

BALLISTITE—A solid propellant, made of nitroglycerin and nitrocellulose.

BALLISTIC MISSILE—A missile, such as a rocket, fired by application of a relatively large amount of force (as thrust) for a short duration. After application of this impulse, the missile then coasts to its destination following the laws of nature.

BALLISTICS—The art and science dealing with the projection or firing of missiles. Applies to both guns and rockets.

BALLISTICS, EXTERNAL—That branch of ballistics which deals with such

163

external forces as effects of gravity, air resistance, etc., on the motion of a missile.

BALLISTICS, INTERNAL—That branch of ballistics which deals with such internal forces as propulsion and launching of missiles.

BI-PROPELLANT—A propellant system employing two separate propellants.

BMEWS—Ballistic missile early warning system.

BOOSTER—Usually a rocket device which first gets a missile moving. Thus, the first or primary launching stage.

BURNOUT—Applies to the time or velocity of a missile when the propellants have been exhausted.

CENTIMETER—A unit of metric length measurement. One centimeter equals 2.54 inches.

CLUSTER—A grouping of rocket engines or entire rockets to form a single-acting unit.

COMBUSTION CHAMBER—This is where the propellants or fuels are burned to form propelling gases.

COMPLEX—Any grouping of industrial plants or military bases which are tied together in a similar function.

COMPOSITE—A type of solid propellant in which oxidizer and fuel are usually in two separate phases.

CORDITE—A type of solid propellant, solvent formed, composed of nitroglycerin, nitrocellulose, and mineral jelly.

COSMIC RADIATION—These rays come in from outer space (origin unknown) and are very penetrating. There are primary cosmic rays, consisting of the nucleus of light atoms, and secondary cosmic rays, caused when the primaries hit the atmosphere.

COUNTERMEASURES—As applied to electronics, the term indicates jamming or otherwise disturbing the electronics of the enemy.

CROSS SECTION—In radar, the apparent image of the target.

CRUISE MISSILE—A missile, usually winged, that flies like an airplane in a horizontal position.

CSAGI—Comité Special de l'Année Geophysicale Internationale, Special Committee for the International Geophysical Year.

DOSAAF—Soviet organization, The All-Union Volunteer Society for the Promotion of the Army, Aviation, and Navy.

DOUBLE BASE—Solid propellants using nitrocellulose and nitroglycerin.

FAIRING—A member or structure, the primary function of which is to produce a smooth outline and to reduce drag or head resistance, as in an aircraft. (Merriam Webster.)

FIX—Radio–electronic jargon for an establishment of position by directional finding equipment.

FREQUENCY—In wave motion, the number of waves passing by in a second.

FUEL—Commonly, a substance which will burn. In a combustion process the fuel furnishes electrons to the oxidizer.

GIGATON—Equal to a billion tons.

HARD BASE—A military base or installation, usually underground, that is built to withstand an atomic explosion.

HARD LANDING—A landing in which the vehicle is allowed to crash into an immovable body such as the earth or another planet and be destroyed by the impact; that is, where no braking forces are used to stop a moving body.

HARDWARE—Jargon for actual equipment, as opposed to a blueprint or a theoretical design.

HOMOGENEOUS—Used to refer to a type of solid propellant in which both oxidizer and fuel are combined in the same phase; opposed to composites.

HYBRID PROPELLANT—A mixed propellant system such as liquid–solid or rocket–ramjet.

HYBRID ROCKET—A system in which the rocket is combined with another type of propulsion medium, e. g. rocket–ramjet.

HYPERSONIC—Applied to vehicles which travel about five times the speed of sound.

IAF—Abbreviation for International Astronautical Federation.

IAPVO—Abbreviation for Soviet Fighter Aviation of Air Defense.

ICBM—Intercontinental ballistic missile, having a range of 5,000 to 10,000 miles.

IGY—International Geophysical Year. A period set aside by world science (July 1957 to January 1959) in a common and coordinated attempt to provide data on the earth and its physical environment.

IMPULSE—In rocketry, an impulse or moving force is the product of thrust and time.

ION—A charged particle, usually an atom.

IRBM—Intermediate range ballistic missile, having a range of 1,000 to 2,000 miles.

IR—Abbreviation for infrared. Infrared waves are located just beyond the visible red waves of the spectrum. They are commonly used for guidance.

KGB—Soviet Committee for State Security.

KILOGRAM—Unit of weight in the metric system, equal to 1,000 grams. One kilogram is equivalent to about 2.2 pounds.

KILOMETER—Unit of length in the metric system, equal to 1,000 meters. One kilometer is equal to about 0.62 miles.

KILOTON—Equal to 1,000 tons.

KOPECK—Unit of Russian money; 100 kopecks make one ruble.

L*—Symbol for characteristic chamber length. This is a rating parameter and is the ratio of the combustion chamber volume over the throat area.

LAUNCHING—Getting a rocket or missile off the ground; the initial phase of flight.

LOX—Abbreviation for liquid oxygen, a common liquid oxidizer. LOX boils at -297° F. and cannot be stored for long. It must be insulated.

LMG—Abbreviation for light machine gun.

LUNIK—Popular name for the Soviet series of moon rockets, from *luna* ("moon") and *sputnik* ("satellite").

MACH—The Mach number is a way of giving the speed of a vehicle in comparison to the speed of sound. Thus, a speed of Mach 1 means the craft travels at the speed of sound; at Mach 3.6, you are going 3.6 times the speed of sound. The speed of sound varies with altitude and with temperature of the air. It is about 760 miles per hour at sea level and about 675 miles per hour at an altitude of 30,000 feet. The term is named after Ernst Mach, Austrian scientist.

MAGNETOHYDRODYNAMICS—That branch of science which deals with the effects of magnetic forces on the flow of gas plasmas.

MASS RATIO—The ratio between the loaded (with propellant) weight of a rocket and its empty weight (after propellant has been burned). This ratio determines the effectiveness of a rocket's performance.

MEGACYCLE—One million cycles. As applied to waves, the number of million cycles passing by in one second.

MEGATON—Equal to 1 million tons.

METEORITES—Particles of matter in outer space traveling at enormous speeds. Meteorites are visible when they enter the earth's atmosphere where they glow due to friction with the air. Most of them burn up before reaching the ground.

METRIC TON—Equal to 2,200 pounds. Commonly called a long ton.

MHD—Abbreviation for magnetohydrodynamics.

MILLIMETER—A unit of metric length. 25.4 millimeters (mm.) are equal to one inch.

MISSILE—Any vehicle (manned or unmanned) which is shot, hurled, or fired at its target. It may be propelled by any number of propulsion systems, viz., rocket, ramjet, or turbojet.

MVD—Soviet Ministry of Internal Affairs.

NASA—United States National Aeronautics and Space Administration. This agency was created from the old National Advisory Committee for Aeronautics (NACA). NASA is a civilian agency and came about after Sputnik I. It marked recognition of the transition of aeronautics to the space sciences.

NOZZLE—The expansion section of a rocket engine which accelerates the burning gases out of the combustion chamber and gives thrust.

ORBIT—The path of a body around another body. Thus, the moon orbits the earth and the earth orbits the sun.

OXIDIZER—Any material which accepts electrons in a combustion reaction. Non-oxygen materials can be oxidizers.

PAYLOAD—The useful or load-carrying portion of a rocket or missile.

PASSIVE—As applied to guidance systems, a device which responds to instructions given it by an external source.

PERIGEE—The closest distance in an orbit.

PHOTON—Light ray or beam.

PLASMA—Concentrated gas source that is electrically or magnetically conductive.

PROBE—An instrumented investigation which seeks some specific information.

PROPELLANT—A combination of fuel and oxidizer which furnishes the energy for propulsion, the driving material. It can be liquid or solid.

PSI. OVERPRESSURE—The pressure (in pounds per square inch) of a blast or shock wave caused by an explosion.

PULSEJET—An intermittent explosion engine. The explosions provide thrusts.

PVO—Soviet Antiair Defense Forces.

PYROTECHNIC—A fire-producing material.

RADAR—From *r*adio *d*etection *a*nd *r*anging, a beam of radio waves of various possible frequencies which are sent out from an antenna. When these waves strike a reflecting surface (such as a metal object), they return. From the return waves it is possible to tell range, direction, and even size of the object.

RADIATION—Energy transmission from one object to another. Radiation can be looked on as having wavelike or particle-like properties.

RAMJET—A form of propulsion system that consists of a cylindrical tube, open at both ends. Fuel is burned with incoming air and ejected at the back end to give thrust, which moves the tube forward. The combustion is prevented from leaving the front end by the compressed air entering which forms a shock wave wall.

RATO—Rocket-assisted takeoff.

REACTOR—A spatial arrangement of nuclear fuels to provide a sustaining chain reaction. Analogous to a rocket combustion chamber; however the nuclear reaction takes place within itself.

RECOVERY—The process whereby a nose cone, capsule, or satellite is safely returned to earth.

RETROROCKET—A rocket which is fired in the opposite direction of flight to provide braking forces.

RETROTHRUST—Thrust opposite to the direction of motion.

ROCKET—A generic term for a device, completely self-sustained, that moves by the action-and-reaction principle. When matter is expelled in one direction, an opposite force or thrust results. This moves the rocket.

ROTI—Abbreviation for Recording Optical Tracking Instrument.

RUBLE—A unit of Russian money. One ruble is equal to about ten cents in United States money, on international exchange. Thus 10 rubles equal $1.00.

SAC—The Strategic Air Command of the United States Air Force.

SATELLITE—Any object, natural or man-made, which revolves around another body.

SCRUB—Termination of a missile launching sequence. Hence, hold or stop.

SHOT—Jargon for missile firing or launch.

SNORKEL—A German World War II development which allows a submarine to travel while under water. Air for engines is brought in through a large tube which has its inlet above the surface of the water.

SOFT BASE—A missile or military base that is vulnerable to atomic attack.

SOFT LANDING—A landing in which braking forces are applied in order to bring a vehicle gently to the surface.

SPECIFIC IMPULSE—A rating of chemical and nuclear propellants. It is equal to the impulse given by a unit weight of propellant. Thus, so many pounds of thrust for so many seconds as given by so many pounds of propellant.

SPIKED FUEL—Fuel with a small amount of high energy component added.

SPUTNIK—Russian word for satellite.

SUPERSONIC—Faster than the speed of sound. (See also note on Mach.)

TAC—Tactical Air Command of the United States Air Force.

TELEMETRY—The process of transmitting information from one point to another, usually via radio waves. Usually used for obtaining information from a rocket and receiving it at a ground station.

TERATON—Equal to 1 trillion tons.

THRUST—The force (usually expressed in terms of so many equivalent pounds of weight) produced by a rocket due to the reaction process.

TOP—To replace vaporized propellant lost during loading operation. Done just before firing.

TOT—Time on target.

TRACKING—Following a rocket or missile, as by radar.

TRAJECTORY—The flight path of a rocket or missile.

TURBOJET—A jet engine that uses a rotating compressor to feed air into a combustion chamber. Moves via the thrust or reaction principle.

UV—Ultraviolet. Waves which are just beyond the violet in the spectrum, at the opposite end from infrared waves.

VNOS—Soviet Air Observation, Report, and Signal Service.

XMTTR—Radio/electronics jargon or abbreviation for transmitter.

WARHEAD—The payload of a military missile which contains chemical or nuclear explosives.

RUSSIAN ROCKETRY ROSTER

Artakinov, Professor. Took over as Soviet director of German Peene-münde test station.

Artamonov, Nickolai F. Soviet naval captain who, in 1959, defected to the West and outlined Soviet surprise attack policy.

Bardin, I.P. Vice President of the Academy of Science. President of the USSR National IGY Committee.

Biryuzov, Sergei S. This marshal heads up all USSR antiaircraft defenses. His AA command is claimed to have shot down the American U-2 spy plane with a rocket. The plane was said to have been shot down from an altitude of 68,000 feet.

Blaganravov, A.A. Member of the presidium of the Academy of Science, also an armaments expert, high in the USSR rocket program.

Dushkin, L.S. Designed 651 lb. rocket engine in 1943.

Glushko, V.P. Designed and built rocket engine during the thirties.

Kapitsa, Peter L. Famous nuclear scientist. Adviser to Sputnik projects. His work in cryogenics was instrumental in development of liquid propellant ballistic rockets.

Karpenko, A.G. Scientific secretary of Commission on Interplanetary Communications.

Kondratyuk, Yu.V. Pupil of Ziolkovsky who advocated multi-stage rockets.

Konstantinov, Konstantin. Father of experimental rocketry in Russia. Advocated standards and methods of testing rockets in the 1800's.

Kriksunov, V. Engineer-major involved in USSR anti-ICBM program.

Kuleshov, P.N. General of artillery who, after World War II, was instrumental in promoting rocket development for weapons purposes.

Lavochkin, Designer of rocket engine in 1946.

Meshchersky I.V. Published work on dynamics of variable masses, applicable to rocketry, in nineteenth century.

Mikhaylov, A.I. Head of All Union Institute of Scientific and Technical information. Responsible for many rocket publications.

Moskalenko, Kirill Semenovich. Took over in October, 1960, as supreme commander of Soviet missile forces after the death of Nedelin.

Nedelin, Mitrofan I. Soviet rocket chief, "Marshall of Rocketry." Built up force of about 200,000 people and some 100 rocket bases. Died in plane crash October 1960.

Nesmeyanov, Alexander N. Head of the USSR Academy of Science. In charge of all USSR research and head of satellite and space research program.

Pokrovski, G.I. This general is involved in an air force nuclear-powered aircraft program.

Rynin, N.A., Compiled astronautical encyclopedia in the USSR during 1928-1932.

Sedov, L.I. President of the Commission on Interplanetary Communications under USSR Academy of Science. Thus, Sedov, an hydrodynamics expert, is high in the rocket program. Also current president of twenty-nine-nation group International Astronautical Federation.

Shternfeld, Ari A. Popular space writer and winner of the International Prize for the Promotion of Astronautics.

Tsander, F.A. Contemporary of Ziolkovsky. He built a LOX-kerosene rocket engine in 1932.

Tsien, H.S. Chinese-American rocket expert who, in 1953, returned to Red China. Director of Institute of Mechanics at the Academia Sinica in Peking. Believed to be leader in Red China's rocket and space efforts.

Yakolev, A.S. This general was early in charge of Office of Special Weapons which fostered development of large ballistic missiles at end of World War II.

Zasyadko, Alexander. A major general in the Czarist Army, designed war rockets in 1817 in St. Petersburg.

Zhigarev, Pavel. Soviet chief of Air Force in the fifties. Gave high support to development of the ICBM. Believed that the ballistic missile would make the airplane bomber obsolete.

Ziolkovsky, Konstantin E. (1857-1935). Father of Russian rocketry.

INDEX

BIOGRAPHICAL NOTE

Born in 1925, Alfred J. Zaehringer attended Southwestern High School in Detroit and later graduated from Wayne State University. From his early childhood, he has been fascinated with rockets. He began seriously to collect all available information on Soviet rocket activities in 1952. After graduation Mr. Zaehringer worked as chemist with the City of Detroit Testing Laboratory, then as Chief Rocket Test Engineer for the Thiokol Chemical Corporation at Elkton, Maryland. In 1954 he established the American Rocket Company in Wyandotte, Michigan, and has been its president since that time.

He is the author of *Solid Propellant Rockets* and has had articles in many scientific journals, such as *Aero Digest, Aviation Age, Engineering Digest, Chemical Abstracts, Ordnance, Journal of Space Flight, Missiles and Rockets,* etc. Professional organizations to which he belongs include American Chemical Society, American Ordnance Association, and American Rocket Society. Among his hobbies are photography, travel, mineralogy, crystallography, gardening, and low-fi.